RAINBOW magic™

101

things to

MAKE

and

Do

ORCHARD BOOKS
338 Euston Road, London NW1 3BH
Orchard Books Australia
Level 17/207 Kent Street, Sydney, NSW 2000

First published in 2015 by Orchard Books

HIT entertainment

Fairy illustrations from *Flora, Summer, Chrissie, Holly, Kylie, Paige, Stella* and books 1-63 © Georgie Ripper.
All other illustrations © Orchard Books 2015, based on underlying copyright owned by Georgie Ripper.

A CIP catalogue record for this book is available
from the British Library.

ISBN 978 1 40833 790 5

1 3 5 7 9 10 8 6 4 2

Printed in China

The paper and board used in this paperback are natural recyclable products made from wood grown in
sustainable forests.
The manufacturing processes conform to the environmental regulations of the country of origin.

Orchard Books is an imprint of Hachette Children's Group
and published by The Watts Publishing Group Limited, an Hachette UK company.

www.hachette.co.uk

Adult supervision is recommended when glue, paint, scissors and other sharp points are in use, and for
activities that require cooking, baking or heating.

RAINBOW magic™

101 things to MAKE and Do

ORCHARD

www.rainbowmagic.co.uk

Contents

101 things to Make and Do

Violet's Magical Rainbow Paint

Violet was so thrilled that the Rainbow Fairies could help save her precious paintbrush! This magical painting is so eye-catching – all you need are some watercolours and a black crayon.

You will need:
- Thin white card
- Watercolour paints
- Black wax crayon
- Old newspapers
- Paintbrush
- Cocktail stick

1

Spread out some old newspaper. Carefully paint rainbow stripes all across the card. Start with a swish of red at the top, then work all your way down to violet. Make sure that every part of the card is covered with paint. Then leave your card to dry.

2

Take a black crayon and colour over your painting. Keep going until the whole sheet of card is black.

3

Now use a cocktail stick to scratch a picture into the black. The crayon will magically fall away, revealing beautiful rainbow colours underneath!

DID YOU KNOW?

There are seven colours in the rainbow: red, orange, yellow, green, blue, indigo and violet.

TOP TIP!

Take some more card, then play with different paint colours and patterns. Will you scratch away the crayon to reveal Queen Titania dressed in a beautiful rainbow skirt, or choose to fill your card with pretty coloured bows and love hearts?

Best Friends Forever!

Do you have a friend with a birthday coming up? Or perhaps you'd like to make a thank-you card, or just one to say hello. Try making this gorgeous card for someone special.

You will need:
- Thin white card
- Pencil
- Scissors
- Felt-tip pens or crayons

1

Take a sheet of card and fold it neatly in half. Press down along the fold and then open out the sheet again.

DID YOU KNOW?
It's not just humans and fairies – animals such as elephants and dolphins have friends too!

2

Flatten the card in front of you, then use a pencil to draw a heart. Make sure that the top half of the heart sits above the fold line and the other half below.

3

Ask a grown-up to help you cut carefully around the top half of the heart. Only cut out the parts of the heart that appear above the fold line.

4

Fold the card flat, then use your favourite felt-tips or crayons to colour the heart in.

5

When you've finished colouring, fold the card back along the crease. Your beautiful heart will pop up at the top!

Try using glittery gel pens or adding stickers to create extra sparkle!

9

Heavenly Hairdo!

Alexa the Fashion Reporter Fairy blushes with pleasure when friends compliment her hairstyle – it's so on-trend! She wears her golden locks in a soft fishtail plait that tumbles down one shoulder.

Matilda the Hair Stylist Fairy came up with Alexa's gorgeous look. This style works best when someone does it for you. If your hair is shoulder-length or longer, find a friend and then give it a whirl!

SSH!
FAIRY SECRET
Matilda loves to mix it up with her own hair! Sometimes her locks have purple highlights, but on other days they have silver or red ones.

1

Make a centre parting down the back of your head and divide your hair into two equal parts.

Take a strand from the outside left. Pull it over the top, then push it under the right and out the other side.

Now do the same thing on the other side, in the opposite direction.

Keep working from the left and right, taking it in turns. Repeat until you've plaited nearly all your hair.

Fix the bottom with a hairband. Give it a light spritz of hairspray then take a peep in the mirror!

What Kind of Fairy Are You?

Indoors or outdoors?

Indoors

Roller disco or sleepover fun?

Disco

Sleepover

Lovely lullabies or magical makeover?

Cool karaoke or twirling to the beat?

Lullabies

Makeover

Karaoke

Twirling

Pampered princess

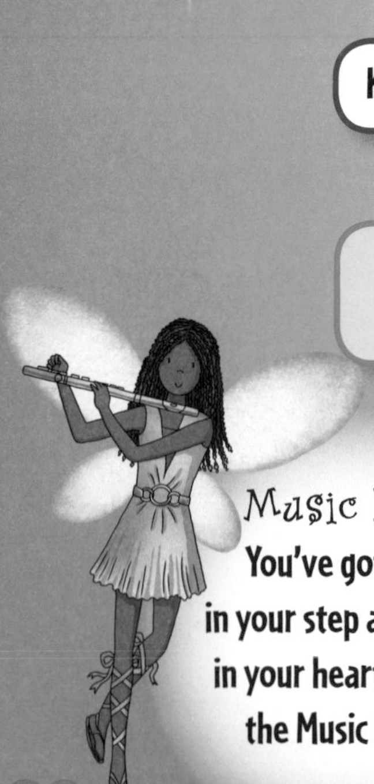

Magical melodies

Dressed divinely

Music Fairy
You've got a skip in your step and a song in your heart, just like the Music Fairies!

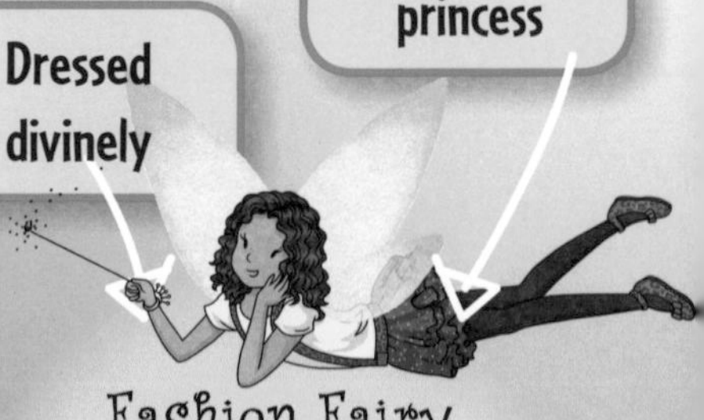

Fashion Fairy
You're a trendsetter who loves dressing up in new outfits. What a fashionista!

12

There are so many beautiful fairies, but which one are you most like?
Answer the questions and work your way down the flowchart.
Your true fairy type will be revealed!

Outdoors → Park play-time or trip to the zoo?

Bat and ball or off to explore? ← Park

Zoo

Bat & Ball — Explore → Cheeky meerkats or cuddly koalas?

Meerkats — Koalas

Sparkling at sports

Fast runners

Cute and cuddly

Sporty Fairy
You're energetic and you always play fair. The Sporty Fairies would love to join your games!

Baby Animal Rescue Fairy
Big or small, cheeky or cuddly, you don't mind a bit – you adore all animals!

13

Happy Heart Pendants

Kirsty and Rachel love the necklaces that their fairy friends gave them. Here's how you can create your own heart necklace for a special friend – try red, gold, green or even rainbow-coloured. Be sure to make them super-sparkly too!

You will need:
- Air-drying modelling clay
- Pencil and paper
- Scissors
- Poster paints and paintbrush
- Jewels or sequins to decorate
- PVA glue
- Thin ribbon

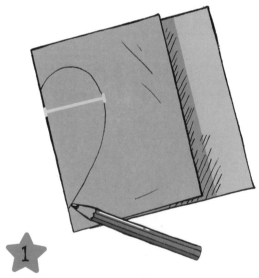

1

Fold the paper in half. Against the folded side, draw half a heart so that it is 1.5cm across at the widest point. You may need an adult to help you.

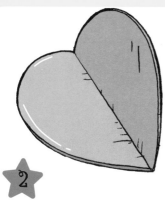

2

Cut out the heart and open it out. This will be the template for making your pendants. Roll out your clay to about 2mm thick.

3

Place the heart on the clay and draw round it with a ballpoint pen or pencil. Remove the clay heart and gently smooth out the edges with your fingers.

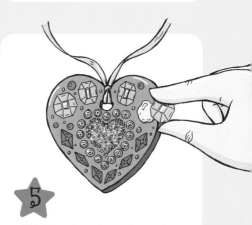

4

Make a hole in the clay heart with the end of your paintbrush. Make sure that it goes all the way through the clay. Leave the clay to dry, then paint it a pretty colour or colours and leave it to dry again.

5

Stick on jewels and sequins with PVA glue. Thread a colourful ribbon through the hole to make a necklace, or hang the heart in your room as a fun fairy decoration.

Flower Fortune-Teller

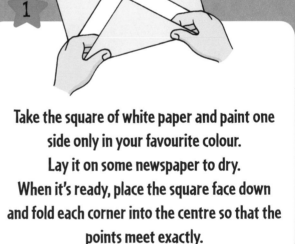

Louise the Lily Fairy loves to hang out with her Petal Fairy friends. Sometimes they take turns reading her pretty water lily fortune-teller. Here's how to make your very own!

You will need:
- A square sheet of white paper approx 21cm x 21cm
- Paintbrush and paint
- Old newspaper
- Felt-tip pens

1

Take the square of white paper and paint one side only in your favourite colour.
Lay it on some newspaper to dry.
When it's ready, place the square face down and fold each corner into the centre so that the points meet exactly.

2

Now turn the square over and fold each corner in again.

16

Fold the square in half along the central line, on the side of the fortune teller that has triangles, as shown here in red. Fold it back and forth a few times until a deep crease is formed.

Put your thumbs and forefingers into each square on the other side of the fortune teller. Move your fingers up and down and left to right a few times to test the fortune teller out. It's nearly ready!

Unfold the paper and turn it painted-side down so that you can write on it. Following the diagram below, use felt-tips to write these words, numbers and phrases onto the square.

Fold your fortune teller back up, following steps 1-4, but with the painted side up. Now find a friend to play with!

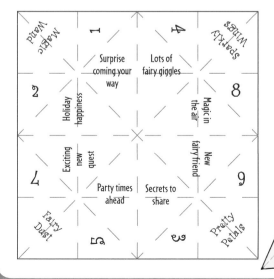

Magic Wand — 1 — 4 — Sparkly Wings
Surprise coming your way | Lots of fairy giggles
2 — Holiday happiness | Magic in the air — 8
Exciting new quest | New fairy friend
7 — Party times ahead | Secrets to share — 6
Fairy Dust — 5 — 3 — Pretty Petals

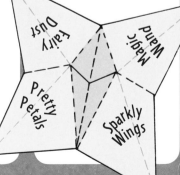

Fairy Dust | Magic Wand | Pretty Petals | Sparkly Wings

17

Jumping Jack Frost!

Jack Frost is always hopping mad about something! Calm him down by sorting out his favourite things from the jumbled words below. Beware, a few of them will make him even angrier – cross them out quickly before he freezes you with an icy bolt from his fingertips!

HILA

_ _ _ _

LCOD

_ _ _ _

BEUL

_ _ _ _

ELATURGH

_ _ _ _ _ _ _ _

Find out if you're right on Page 204

WONS

_ _ _ _

SHINENUS

_ _ _ _ _ _ _ _

SLIGOBN

_ _ _ _ _ _ _ _

FAISEIR

_ _ _ _ _ _ _

19

Wonderful Wind Chimes

Chrissie the Wish Fairy adores the sound of wind chimes ringing in the breeze – it's the closest thing to fairy music that you can find in the human world! This magical make-it is just the thing to hang near your bedroom window.

You will need:

- Small terracotta plant pot, 10 cm deep
- Kitchen towel
- Acrylic paints
- Silver string
- Tape measure
- Old newspapers
- Paintbrush
- Scissors
- 2 double-holed buttons
- Noisy items such as metal beads, washers and nuts
- Heavy decorative beads

1

Wash the terracotta pot in soapy water and pat it dry with kitchen towel.

2

Place the pot on some old newspapers, then paint bands of rainbow colours round the edge, working your way up to the top.

3

Leave the pot to dry overnight.

4

Unroll a ball of silver string, then cut off a piece at least 50cm long.

5

Turn your pot upside down. Find two buttons that are bigger than the hole in the bottom of the pot. Take one and thread the silver string through its first hole. Now push the string back through the other hole to create a loop.

6

Instead of pulling the loop tight, tie a knot in it above the button. Later you will use this loop to hang up your wind chime!

7

Carefully slip the ends of the string through the hole in the top of the pot so that the loop and button sit on top of it.

8

Now thread the ends of the string through the second button and push it up so it is inside the pot, holding it in place. Tie a tight double knot to secure the button in position.

9

Thread a variety of beads and washers onto the string, tying them at different levels. Make sure they are all short enough to hang inside the pot.

10

Snip off the bottom of each length of string, so that it hangs around 10cm below the rainbow pot.

11

Finally, tie heavy beads to each string, ready to catch the breeze.

Gingerbread Goblins!

Jack Frost's goblins stir up so much trouble for the Rainbow Magic Fairies! This gingerbread recipe will help you get your own back on the green meanies. Not only are they fun to make, the goblin-shaped biscuits taste delicious, too!

1

Ask a grown-up to set the oven to 190°C/375°F/ Gas Mark 5. Grease two baking trays with some margarine and put them to one side.

2

Put the flour, bicarbonate of soda, ginger and butter into a bowl and rub the mixture gently between your fingers and thumbs.

3

Add the brown sugar, golden syrup, egg and several drops of green food colouring, stirring the mixture until it becomes a firm, green dough. Keep adding extra drops of colouring until you get a good gobliny shade!

4

Use a rolling pin to roll the dough out on a floured surface.

5

Use the cutter to carefully push out your gingerbread goblins. Lay each of them, spaced apart, on the baking trays. Roll the remaining dough out again and cut out more goblins.

6

Put the goblins in the oven and bake them for 15 minutes. Leave them to firm up for a couple of minutes before placing them on a wire rack to cool.

7

Now get creative! Use the black icing pen to draw on a mouth, a big nose and grumpy eyes. With the purple one, give each goblin a raggedy outfit!

23

Pop Star Puzzle

Oh dear! Destiny the Pop Star Fairy has got dressed up for a photoshoot, but something has gone wrong with the pictures.
Only one of these snaps perfectly matches the original. Can you spot which one it is?

A

B

C

D

25

Make a Party Piñata!

Belle the Birthday Fairy flutters all over Fairyland, making sure that everyone has a great time on their birthday! For extra-special occasions, she likes to surprise her friends with a party piñata. Would you like to make one too?

You will need:

- A balloon
- 50g flour
- Measuring jug
- Old newspapers, torn into strips
- Paintbrush
- Coloured poster paint
- Bright strips of crepe paper
- PVA glue
- Scissors
- Pencil
- Household string

1
Blow up your balloon then ask a grown-up to tie a knot in the end.

2
Dip strips of newspaper into the glue, then lay them on the balloon. Keep draping on pieces of paper until the entire balloon is covered.

3
Measure the flour into a plastic bowl, then stir in 150ml of tap water. Give the mixture a good stir – this will be the glue that holds your piñata together!

26

4

When the balloon has dried out, paste on a second and then a third layer of newspaper. Make sure you allow plenty of time between building up each new layer, so that the paste can set properly.

5

Choose the brightest colour you can find, then paint the piñata all over. Set the piñata to one side so that it can dry out again.

6

When the piñata is dry, ask a grown-up to pop the balloon inside.

7

Wind an eye-catching strip of crepe paper around the top of the piñata, dotting PVA glue along the upper edge. Work your way down, sticking more rows of crepe in place. When you reach the bottom your piñata should be completely trimmed with pretty frills!

8

Ask a grown-up to push a pencil through the top of the piñata at either side of the hole made by the balloon. Loop a piece of string through the small holes, then tie it in a knot to make a hook. Now it's party time!

Almost Bedtime!

Willow the Wednesday Fairy has had a very busy day and is looking forward to going to bed. But the goblins have been casting pesky spells! There are five things here that you don't normally see in a bedroom. Can you find them?

DID YOU KNOW?
We spend over one-third of our lives asleep!

Find out if you're right on Page 204

29

Iced Thunderbolt Biscuits

Stop Jack Frost in his tracks by eating up his icy thunderbolts! Ask an adult to help you bake these yummy biscuits.

You will need:

FOR THE SHORTBREAD:

- 125g butter
- 55g caster sugar
- 180g plain flour, plus extra for dusting
- 1 teaspoon vanilla extract
- Salt

FOR THE ICING:

- 200g icing sugar
- Warm water
- Blue food colouring (optional)

1

In a bowl, mix the butter and caster sugar together with a wooden spoon until you have a smooth, fluffy mixture.

2

Next, stir in the vanilla extract. Then add the flour and a little pinch of salt, and stir until the mixture has formed into a ball.

flour

salt

3

Sprinkle flour on a work surface. Then use a rolling pin to roll the ball out. Keep going until it is about 1 cm thick.

4

Draw a thunderbolt shape onto the piece of paper and cut it out. You can use it as a template to cut your biscuits from.

5

Place your template onto the dough and cut around it. Repeat until all the dough is used. Put the shapes on the baking trays and into the fridge for 20 minutes. Set the oven to 190°C/375°F/Gas Mark 5.

6

Take the trays from the fridge and ask an adult to put them in the oven for about 15 minutes, or until the thunderbolts are golden.

7

Ask an adult to take the trays out of the oven. When the trays are cool, take the biscuits off and place them on a wire rack.

8

Sift the icing sugar into a bowl. Add warm water little by little, until the mixture is smooth but not too runny. If you are using food colouring, add a few drops to the bowl. Finally, ice the biscuits and leave to set!

31

Musical Miss Quiz!

Maya, Danni and the other Music Fairies know the true power of a sweet melody. There's nothing like a pretty tune to bring a smile to your face, or a rousing beat to get you up on your feet. Take this quick quiz to discover which kind of music moves you...

1 Your favourite colour is...
- ☐ A. Pink
- ☐ B. Purple
- ☐ C. Yellow
- ☐ D. Red

4 At school you're best at...
- ☐ A. Art
- ☐ B. Science
- ☐ C. English
- ☐ D. Drama

2 Your best friend would describe you as...
- ☐ A. Bubbly and fun
- ☐ B. Outgoing and crazy
- ☐ C. Quiet and thoughtful
- ☐ D. Dramatic and dreamy

5 Your favourite way to spend an afternoon is...
- ☐ A. Friends make-overs
- ☐ B. Playground
- ☐ C. Reading a book
- ☐ D. Dressing up

3 The instrument you'd most like to play is...
- ☐ A. Saxophone
- ☐ B. Guitar
- ☐ C. Violin
- ☐ D. Piano

6 The sweet treat you like the best is...
- ☐ A. Bubblegum
- ☐ B. Rocky road
- ☐ C. Victoria sponge
- ☐ D. Chocolate bar

Mostly As
YOU'RE A POP PRINCESS
You love music that gets people moving! You are just like Sadie – you can't get enough of her cool clothes and awesome sounds.

Mostly Bs
YOU'RE A ROCK CHICK
You love a thumping tune with a solid beat! Ellie and Danni would be proud of you – you're a true talent!

Mostly Cs
YOU'RE A CLASSICAL GIRL
Music brings peace to your life. You'd love to play a classical instrument like Victoria, Fiona or Maya – perhaps you already do!

Mostly Ds
YOU'RE A MUSICAL MAESTRO
You adore music, but never more than when you're making it yourself, just like Poppy the Piano Fairy!

Eleanor's Jewelled Hair Comb

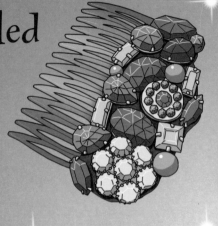

Eleanor's magical hair comb helps her to make sure that her special fairy tale has a happy ending! You can sparkle just like this fabulous fairy with this gorgeous, glittery hair accessory.

You will need:

- A plastic hair comb
- Gems and jewels in a variety of sizes and colours
- Glue
- A piece of felt
- Scissors
- A needle and thread

1

Using your scissors, cut a shape out of the felt, a little larger than the width of your hair comb.

2

Select the gems and jewels you would like to go on your hair comb. Choose a variety of rainbow colours and sparkly styles! Arrange these on the piece of felt and make sure these are grouped tightly together so the material can't be seen.

3

When you are happy with your selection of jewels and gems, stick or glue these onto the felt.

4

Once the glue is dry and the gems are set in place, trim the felt.

5

Now you need the help of a grown-up! Ask your grown-up helper to thread the needle and carefully stitch the felt to the front of the comb.

Clara's Sleepytime Chocolate

Here is Clara the Chocolate Fairy's recipe for a truly delicious hot, chocolaty drink. Yum! Just make sure you keep it out of the way of greedy goblins...

You will need:
- 1 mugful of milk
- 40g dark chocolate, broken into small pieces

1
Pour the milk into a pan and ask an adult to help you heat it until it's almost bubbling.

2
Now remove your pan from the heat and tip in the chocolate. Stir gently until it all melts.

3
Carefully pour the hot chocolate into the mugs.

Chocolate helps your brain release a special hormone that makes you feel happy. Plus, it's delicious!

DID YOU KNOW?

Selena the Sleepover Fairy loves having Clara at her sleepovers, as she always makes this yummy drink for everyone to enjoy!

BE CAREFUL

It might take a few minutes for your hot chocolate to be cool enough to drink.

Kayla's Lovely Letters

Have you ever tried modelling with salt dough? Let Kayla show you how! You don't need a pottery workshop – anyone can make these letters at home and bake them in the oven.

1

Heat the oven to 180°C/350°F/Gas Mark 4. Mix the flour, salt and water together in a bowl. If the salt dough looks too dry and crumbly, tip in a little more water and stir.

2

When the mixture becomes a gooey lump, take it out and knead it with your hands. Now you're ready to start modelling!

You will need:
- 500g flour
- 300g salt
- 250ml water
- Newspapers
- Poster paint
- Paintbrush
- PVA glue
- Glitter
- Clear varnish

3

Pull off a piece of dough and shape it into a letter. You could spell out your name! Lay each letter onto a baking tray.

4

Bake the letters in the oven for about 1 hour. When hardened, ask a grown-up to take them out and cool them on a wire rack.

5

Over some old newspapers, paint each letter in a bright colour. Make sure that the whole shape is covered, on both sides.

6

When the paint is dry, dot some PVA glue over the letters and sprinkle glitter over the top. Then add a layer of clear varnish to make the letters really gleam.

7

Your sparkly letters are ready to put on display! Use them to jazz up a bookshelf, or wrap them in tissue and surprise a friend.

Silly Speak

It looks like Jack Frost has been causing trouble again! Someone has jumbled these fairy quotes into the wrong order. Read the words, look at the pictures, then draw lines to reveal who said what.

A. "Do you like my pink shell ankle bracelets? They jangle as I swim!"

B. "My magical object is a gold tiara with a red jewel in the centre."

C. "I have three precious objects – a memory book, a ribbon and a friendship bracelet."

Florence the Friendship Fairy

Honor the Happy Days Fairy

Find out if you're right on Page 204

Tamara the Tooth Fairy

Juliet the Valentine Fairy

E. "I'm always extra busy on February 14th!"

D. "My favourite day is October 31st – as long as people don't get too scared!"

F. "I have a moonstone ring, an endless coin and a magical pouch."

Trixie the Halloween Fairy

Shannon the Ocean Fairy

41

Beautiful Bookmark!

This is the perfect present for a friend who loves reading! Hannah the Happy Ever After Fairy made one of these pretty bookmarks for each of her friends the Fairytale Fairies, using each fairy's favourite colours.

You will need:

- Several pieces of ribbon in a range of colours. Each piece should be at least 25cm long and some should be wider than others
- Gems, pearls and buttons in a variety of sizes and colours
- Glue
- Scissors
- Ruler
- Pen

First, choose two pieces of ribbon. One should be wider than the other. It's this wider ribbon that will form the base of your bookmark.

Place the widest ribbon on a hard surface and cut it to approximately 25cm in length. Using a pen, make small marks along the centre of the ribbon, approximately 5cm apart.

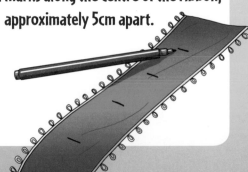

3

Next, fold the ribbon in half lengthways and use your scissors to cut a slit in the ribbon by each of the pen marks. Make sure you don't cut up to the edges of your ribbon!

4

Now cut your second, thinner ribbon to approximately 25cm in length. When this is done, carefully weave this ribbon through the holes in the first ribbon.

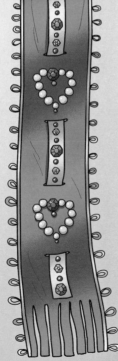

5

Now use some of your self-adhesive gems to decorate the bookmark. If the bookmark is a gift, why not create your friend's initial on the ribbon, or make a pretty flower design?

6

A fringe on your bookmark will look really pretty but adding this is a little bit fiddly, so ask a grown-up for help at this stage. They need to carefully cut up approximately 2cm from the end of the ribbon. The cuts should be around 1mm apart.

A Wand That Goes Whoosh!

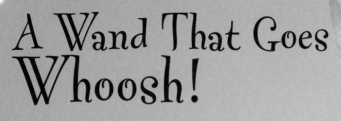

Every Rainbow Magic fairy has an enchanted wand! Here's how to make your own signature wand – all you need are nimble fingers and a mind for magic.

You will need:
- A wooden chopstick
- Poster paint
- Paintbrush
- Thin satin ribbon
- Scissors
- Spray adhesive
- Glitter

1

Lay out some old newspapers and then paint the chopstick. When the chopstick has dried, pick out a length of satin ribbon in a pretty colour.

DID YOU KNOW?

The ancient Druids used wands as far back as 500 BC.

2

Spiral the ribbon up and down the wand. Start from the wide end of the chopstick and leave 20 cm of ribbon spare.

Why not try decorating your wand?
Silk flowers, strings of beads and sequins
or a star shape will all look exquisite!

⭐ 3

When you wind the ribbon back to the base, leave another 20 cm extra before tying the ends in a bow.

⭐ 4

Ask a grown-up to lightly cover the entire wand in spray adhesive.

⭐ 5

Sprinkle glitter up and down the length of the wand and shake off the excess. Your sparkly wand is ready to dazzle your friends!

A Magical Mystery!

Kirsty and Rachel were roller-skating in
Tippington when they came across
the most wonderful fairy! Can you
guess who it was? Read the clues,
look at the silhouette, then
fill in the mystery
fairy's name.

Clues

She is the keeper of the True Love Crown.

She carries a trailing bouquet of flowers.

Her gown is made of delicate ivory silk.

The fairy's name is...

_____

_____

still not sure?

Here's an extra clue. All of these letters feature in her name.

K A E L A D
W E Y G N D
O R I T

Find out if you're right on Page 204

47

Perfect Party Bag

The Party Fairies would hardly have any magic at all if it wasn't for their seven enchanted party bags! Why not stitch your own little bag in your favourite fairy colours? You could fill it with sweet things, lip gloss or a pretty hairclip!

You will need:

- 50 square cm net fabric
- 34 square cm lining fabric
- Scissors
- Fabric glue
- 10 square cm card
- A roll of thin elastic cord
- Needle (suitable for threading elastic cord)
- Approx 40 cm of coloured ribbon

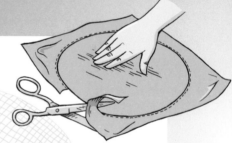

Cut the net fabric into a circle that is about 22cm across the middle. Cut the lining fabric into a circle about 17cm across.

Spread out the fabric circle on a flat surface. Squeeze a thin line of glue round the outer edge of the fabric.

3

Stick the net circle on top of the fabric circle, leaving about 5cm of net around the edge. Allow the glue to dry.

4

Use the needle to thread the elastic in and out of the net just outside the fabric circle. Pull the ends of the elastic tight and tie them together. Cut off the extra elastic.

5

Turn the circles over so the fabric is on top. Cut the card into a circle about 10cm across. Glue the card to the middle of the fabric circle.

6

Cut two small holes in the net about 10cm apart. Thread the ribbon through the holes and tie into a bow. Use the ribbon as a handle for your party bag.

Daisy's Summer Smoothie

Bananas, milk and a touch of honey – what more could a fairy wish for? Daisy the Festival Fairy loves making this scrummy smoothie for her friends! She sometimes adds raspberries from the Fairyland gardens for that little extra touch.

You will need:

- 1 peeled, sliced ripe banana
- 250ml chilled whole milk
- 1 tbsp honey
- 4 or 5 raspberries (optional)

1

Pour the milk into a blender.

2

Add the banana, and the raspberries if you have them.

3

Add the honey. Then blend the ingredients until smooth. Pour into tall glasses. Add a straw and enjoy!

51

Let's Draw Ruby!

Draw a fantastic picture of Ruby the Red Fairy, using these pages as a guide. All you need is a piece of paper, a pencil and some felt-tipped pens or colouring pencils. With a little practice, you'll be picture-perfect in no time!

1

First draw a circle for Ruby's head. Now sketch in some lines to represent the main parts of her body. You could trace these from this picture.

2

Sketch in the shape of Ruby's lovely dress.

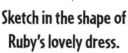

3

Now add the neck, arms and legs. Don't forget to draw in the shapes of her hands and feet!

4

It's time to add the outlines of Ruby's fluttery wings and her magical wand.

6

Now draw Ruby's face, arms and hands. Add her necklace, finish her hair and complete her pretty ballet pumps and ribbons!

5

Draw Ruby's hair and add detail to her dress. Sketch out the ribbons on her legs.

7

Go over the final outline in a black fineliner pen, then rub out the sketch. Now colour your picture and add stars and fairy dust all around Ruby. Well done!

Perfect Pairs

Lila and Myla the Twins Fairies know that all the best things come in pairs! Naughty Jack Frost has got these objects into a muddle. Draw lines to match each picture up to its perfect pair.

Find out if you're right on Page 204

Kayla's Autumn Dish

Kayla just loves to make beautiful dishes at her magical pottery wheel, but you don't have to be the perfect potter to make a pretty dish or bowl! This simple craft is perfect for displaying stunning autumn leaves and pretty berries.

You will need:
- PVA glue
- 1 cup of cold water
- 1 bowl
- Newspaper
- 1 balloon
- Poster paint

1
In a small bowl, mix together two parts PVA glue to one part water (e.g. 500ml of glue to 250ml of water).

2
Tear several sheets of newspaper into strips, roughly the same size.

3

Ask a grown-up to blow up a round balloon to approximately the size of your head, then tie this at the end.

4

Carefully cover around half of the balloon in your glue mix and then layer newspaper on top of the glue. You will need to do this until there are at least three layers of newspaper.

5

Hang the balloon up by the tied end and leave to dry for at least 2-3 days.

6

When the paper is completely dry, pop the balloon using a pin. Ask a grown-up to use scissors to help you trim the shape. Here is your bowl!

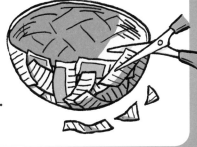

7

Now paint your bowl. When it is dry, fill it with autumn treasures!

What's in Belle's Bag?

What do fairies carry in their handbags? Would you like to see? Belle the Birthday Fairy has emptied out her golden clutch bag. Look at the enchanted objects for one minute, then cover this page and try to complete the quiz on the right.

Birthday Book

HAPPY BIRTHDAY

Belle's Quiz!

It's time to put your fairy spotting skills to the test! Find a pen or pencil, then work your way though the quiz.

1. What colour was Belle's birthday candle?

_____

2. Who were shown in the photo?

_____

3. What things does Belle keep in her bag to make her look pretty?

_____

4. What picture was on the front of the birthday book?

_____

5. What was stitched on Belle's pretty handkerchief?

_____

6. What was stored inside the glass bottle?

_____

7. What colour was the bow on Belle's magical birthday present?

_____

8. How many objects were there inside Belle's clutch bag?

_____

Flowers for Friends

Do you know someone who needs cheering up? Tia the Tulip Fairy has an idea that will make them feel truly special! When she wants to do something kind for a fairy friend, Tia creates a bouquet of these stunning paper flowers.

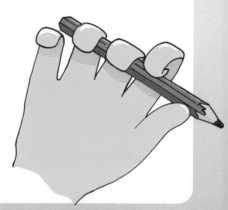

You will need:

- Green pipe-cleaner
- Coloured paper
- Tissue paper
- Sticky tape
- Scissors
- Ribbon
- Stapler
- Pencil

1

Trace your hand onto a sheet of coloured paper, then carefully cut it out.

2

Wrap each finger of the paper hand around a pencil, then release it so that it curls. Make sure you curl each finger in the same direction.

3

Now wrap the palm of the paper hand into a tight cone, with the petals curling outwards. Tape it in place.

4

On a separate sheet of green paper, draw some long leaf shapes. Being very careful with your scissors, cut each one out.

5

Staple the rolled paper hand to the top of a pipe cleaner, then staple one or two leaves halfway down. Your first flower is ready!

6

Repeat the steps until you have made enough flowers to form a lovely bunch. Wrap the flowers in a square of tissue paper and tie it in place with a bright ribbon.

Wand Wordsearch

Ruby's wand is very special. It makes tiny scarlet flowers. What do the other fairies' wands make? This wordsearch is hiding the answers. Look at each fairy picture, then write in the special thing that appears at the end of their wands.

Fern the Green Fairy
_____

Alexa the Fashion Reporter Fairy
_____

Emma the Easter Fairy
_____

Morgan the Midnight Fairy
_____

Summer the Holiday Fairy
_____

62

Storm the Lightning Fairy
_____

Lucy the Diamond Fairy
_____

E	A	S	T	E	R	E	G	G	N
D	G	N	I	N	T	H	G	I	L
R	I	B	F	T	C	W	G	U	K
Y	P	A	X	S	H	E	L	L	C
I	E	D	M	N	M	K	D	E	I
L	N	H	V	O	L	D	C	P	T
R	O	X	A	Z	N	B	L	T	S
H	E	A	R	T	L	D	O	V	P
I	Z	K	W	Q	S	G	C	F	I
S	N	O	W	F	L	A	K	E	L

Leah the Theatre Fairy
_____

Miranda the Beauty Fairy
_____

Find out if you're right on Page 205

63

Magical Microphone

Meet Destiny the Pop Star Fairy – isn't she fabulous? Destiny just loves to sing up a storm – she's a magical performer! With this glittery microphone, you can join her in a dynamic duet.

You will need:
- Kitchen roll tube
- Scissors
- Old newspaper
- Paintbrush
- Gold paint
- Several sheets of dark-coloured tissue paper
- Silver or gold glitter
- Sticky tape
- PVA glue
- 2 buttons
- Glitter
- Stickers

Ask an adult to help you cut the kitchen roll in half, so that you are left with two shorter tubes. Discard one tube half, or give it to a friend so that she can make a mic too!

Lay out some old newspapers and then paint the kitchen tube with gold paint. Leave it to dry.

3

Scrunch up the tissue paper into a ball and insert it into one end of the kitchen roll to make the top of the microphone. Fix it in place with sticky tape.

4

Tape or glue two buttons in a vertical line on the kitchen roll handle, so that they resemble on/off buttons.

5

Now give your mic some pop star glitz by adding glitter and as many stickers as you like!

Why not try writing your own song about Destiny, then ask a friend to sing it with you?

Fairy Fashion

Headwear
A. Over-sized cap worn to one side
B. Sparkly tiara
C. Hair comb decorated with roses
D. Beret with little badges pinned on

Accessories
A. Chunky belt
B. Clutch bag decorated with sequins
C. Masses of big, gold bangles
D. Heart-shaped sunglasses

Mostly As

You're the true queen of casual, happiest in trousers and unfussy tops! Pumps, cropped jeans, funky tees and gingham shirts would all work well with your chilled-out style!

Mostly Bs

You're the ultimate glamour puss, a trendy party girl who dresses to impress. You like to see a new look every time you step in front of your bedroom mirror!

What's your true fairy style? Try this quiz to find out – work down from top to toe, picking the item that you like best each time.

Tops

A. Vest top in a bright colour
B. Shiny halter-neck
C. Ruffled wrap-top
D. Stripy scoop-neck

Skirts, Dresses and Trousers

A. Cargo trousers
B. Puff-ball mini with leggings
C. Long, layered skirt stitched with tingly bells
D. Vintage prom dress

Shoes

A. Funky trainers with wheelie heels
B. Trendy knee-high boots
C. Roman-style sandals
D. Cute buckled Mary-Janes

Mostly Cs

Your bold style is eye-catching, colourful and full of fun. You look sensational in ra-ra skirts, threaded gypsy tops and embroidered denim.

Mostly Ds

You are the princess of vintage! Your ability to mix and match old and new clothes gives you a signature style that is all your very own.

Eleanor's Fairytale Castle

When Kirsty and Rachel went to the Fairytale Festival, they got to stay in Tiptop Castle – a wonderful old building with towers and turrets. Here are Eleanor's tips on making a sparkly fairytale castle of your own!

You will need:
- 4 empty kitchen roll tubes
- Small cardboard box
- Scissors
- Sticky tape
- Poster paint
- Paintbrush
- Felt-tip pens or markers
- PVA glue
- Thin coloured card

1

Cut the top flaps off the cardboard box. Keep them for later.

2

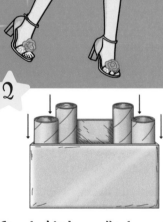

Stand a kitchen roll tube upright in each of the corners of the box. Trim the tops down so that they stand about 6 cm taller than the box. Tape them into position.

3

Choose a colour, and paint the castle inside and out. Leave it to dry.

4

Take one of the flaps and cut out a large door shape. Paint it and leave to dry.

5

Draw some detail onto the door. Add a handle, keyhole and maybe a peephole, too. When you've finished, glue the door onto the front of the castle wall.

6

Using a saucer, cut out two circles from a piece of card. Cut them in half and roll up each semi-circle into a roof turret. Tape a turret to the top of each of the kitchen-roll tubes.

7

Now it's time to decorate! Maybe add some magical sparkles, or a fairy at the window? This part is up to you!

Alison's Magical Mosaics

Queen Titania is hosting a Butterfly Ball and she's asked Alison to make the decorations! The Art Fairy has decided to fill the palace with beautiful mosaics, and her art students are going to help. Perhaps some of your friends would like to help with yours?

You will need:

- Old magazines, giftwrap or coloured paper
- Scissors
- A handful of envelopes
- Thin black card
- White chalk or pencil
- PVA glue
- Paintbrush
- Glitter pens

1

Take your giftwrap, magazine or coloured paper and cut it into lots of small square shapes about a centimetre wide.

2

Separate them out so that you keep all of the same colour squares together in a pile.

3

Put each pile of scraps into an envelope and write the colour on the front so you can find it again easily.

4

Use chalk or a white pencil to draw the outline of a butterfly as large as you can on the black card.

DID YOU KNOW?
The Ancient Romans liked to fill their palaces and homes with mosaics.

5

Mix some glue and water in a saucer. Dab it over a small section of the butterfly's wing with a paintbrush.

6

Using your brush, take out the coloured scraps and stick them onto the wing, until the whole glued section is covered.

7

Move onto the next section of the butterfly, adding paper mosaics one-by-one. You can fill a space with one single colour, or mix things up a bit!

8

When the entire butterfly is covered with scraps, use glitter pens to add wing detail and antennae. Beautiful!

71

Tamara's Enchanted Pouch

Tamara the Tooth Fairy makes all the teeth she collects into fairy dust, and keeps it in her enchanted pouch. Why not make a pouch of your own? Then when your next tooth falls out you can put it in the pouch, ready for the tooth fairy to collect!

You will need:
- A piece of soft fabric
- Saucer
- Newspaper
- Marker pen
- Gold thread
- Scissors
- Sticky tape
- Your tooth, when the next one falls out!

1

Place the fabric on top of the newspaper, softest side down.

2

Put the saucer on top of the fabric and draw round it with your marker pen.

3

Ask a grown-up to help you cut along the line you've drawn.

4

Next, cut three long strands of gold thread and tie the ends together with a small knot. Attach the knotted end to a work surface, using some sticky tape.

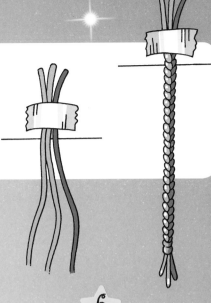

5

Plait the threads together and tie a knot at the bottom.

6

Place your tooth in the centre of the fabric.

7

Bunch the fabric up around the tooth, and tie it at the top with the gold plait.

8

Place the pouch under your pillow, and wait for Tamara to arrive. Sweet dreams!

Magical Mermaid Mobile

Lacey just loves looking after the Little Mermaid fairy tale! Here's how to make a magical mobile decorated with shimmering mermaids.

You will need:

FOR THE MOBILE
- An embroidery hoop. Ideally this should be at least 6 inches (15cm) in diameter.
- A ball of string
- Scissors
- Ruler

FOR THE MERMAIDS
- Plain card
- Pens and pencils
- Glitter pen or glitter to decorate

Mobile

Using your ruler, measure out six lengths of string. These should vary in length from approximately 15cm to 40cm. Cut out each one using your scissors.

Ask your grown-up helper to tie these pieces of string around your embroidery hoop, leaving equal spaces between each. Start with the longest length of string, then the next longest and so on. This will create a spiral-like appearance for your final mobile.

Magical Mermaids

On your piece of card, draw an oval shape for your mermaid's head, connected to a larger oval shape with a flat bottom.

4

Now it's time to draw a curved tail! Don't forget a flappy fin. Next add a pretty shell necklace around your mermaid's neck.

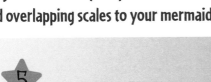

3

Add arms and hair to your mermaid. Why not give each of your six mermaids a different hairstyle? Add some gorgeous detail to your picture! Draw a smiley face and add overlapping scales to your mermaid's tail.

5

When you've drawn six mermaids, carefully cut them out using your scissors. Now colour them in. Add the finishing touch to your pictures by using your glitter pens so that your mermaids sparkle as they spin in the air!

Animal Match-Ups

Can you match each fairy with her pet? Draw a line between them, using a different coloured crayon or felt-tip pen for each.

Bella the Bunny Fairy

Harriet the Hamster Fairy

Lauren the Puppy Fairy

Twinkle

Sunny

Misty

Find out if you're right on Page 205

Georgia the
Guinea Pig
Fairy

Katie the
Kitten Fairy

Molly the
Goldfish Fairy

Penny the
Pony Fairy

Glitter

Flash

Sparky

Shimmer

77

Lizzie's Fairy Bread Pudding

Lizzie the Sweet Treats Fairy is always tempting her friends with delicious makes and bakes. She just loves sweet things! This dessert recipe is both healthy and delicious.

You will need:

- 2 tbsp margarine
- 6 slices fruit bread
- 75g dried apricots
- 2 eggs
- 1 tsp vanilla extract
- 450ml semi-skimmed milk

1

Ask a grown-up to heat the oven to 180°C/350°F/Gas Mark 4. Grease a baking dish with some of the margarine, then spread the rest on the bread slices. Cut each slice into four triangles, and layer in rows in the baking dish.

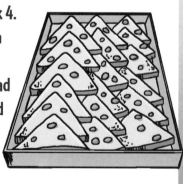

78

2

Carefully slice the apricots into little pieces and sprinkle them over the bread.

3

Crack the eggs into a mixing bowl, then mix in the vanilla extract and the milk. Pour the mixture over the bread in the baking dish, then cover it with plastic food wrap.

4

When the milk has soaked into the bread for at least 30 minutes, it's ready to go into the oven. Take off the food wrap and bake it for 40 minutes.

**SSH!
FAIRY SECRET**
Roxie the Baking Fairy loves to spend wintry days cooking up sweet treats with Lizzie!

79

Spot the Difference

Doesn't this picture make you hungry? Here are two peckish Sporty Fairies stopping for a yummy picnic. Can you spot eight differences between the pictures? Circle them on the right-hand picture.

Find out if you're right on Page 205

The word "picnic" comes from the French word "pique-nique", meaning "to pick at small things".

Dance with Giselle

Giselle the Christmas Ballet Fairy is such a graceful dancer – when she pirouettes it looks like she's walking on air! Every morning she stretches at the barre and works on her positions. All ballerinas have to practise the basic ballet positions. There are only five to remember, but they are very important. Would you like to join today's class? Find a space in your bedroom or garden and copy Giselle's moves.

SSH!
FAIRY SECRET
Giselle's best friend is Bethany the Ballet Fairy. The two of them often practise together!

Stand with your heels touching and your toes turned out. Curl your arms neatly in front of you.

Slide your feet a little further apart, then lift and open your arms.

Cross one foot in front of the other. Curve one arm in front of you and hold the other out to the side.

Keeping a small gap between your feet, reach one arm up. Curl your other arm out in front of you.

Put your feet together and reach both your arms up above your head. What a beautiful ballerina!

Create a Card!

Each year, Annabelle the Drawing Fairy uses her special magic to send homemade Christmas cards to her family and friends! Here's how to make your very own magical 3D fairy card this Christmas.

You will need:

- A plain sheet of card
- Scissors
- A pencil
- Glitter pens, colouring pens and pencils and stickers to decorate your card

1

Ask a grown-up to cut out your card base from the sheet of card. When folded, the front of the card should be around 15cm long and 10cm wide.

2

Fold another similar-sized piece of card in half and draw one half of a simple fairy shape. Cut it out and open up the shape. This is the template for your 3D fairy!

3

Place your template on the front of your card and draw around it. Make a small mark near the fairy's head and another by her feet. These are there to remind you not to cut out the fairy completely in step 4. Put the fairy template to one side.

4

Cut around the fairy on the front of the card. Don't forget, she needs to be attached to the card by her head and her feet!

5

Now push out the wings of the fairy from the front of the card so it stands out.

6

Now it's time to decorate your fairy! Use your colouring pens and pencils to draw a face, colour in her pretty wings and add a Christmassy outfit. Why not make her look like your favourite Rainbow Magic fairy? Don't forget to decorate the card background, too.

A Royal Message

King Oberon and Queen Titania have a special message for you! They've used a magical code to disguise the message, so mean Jack Frost can't read it. Are you clever enough to crack the code by writing the human letters underneath the fairy letters?

Human letter		Fairy letter		Human letter		Fairy letter		Human letter		Fairy letter
A	=	X		J	=	G		S	=	P
B	=	Y		K	=	H		T	=	Q
C	=	Z		L	=	I		U	=	R
D	=	A		M	=	J		V	=	S
E	=	B		N	=	K		W	=	T
F	=	C		O	=	L		X	=	U
G	=	D		P	=	M		Y	=	V
H	=	E		Q	=	N		Z	=	W
I	=	F		R	=	O				

M I B X P B   Z L J B   Q L
PLEASE COM_E TO A

X   Y X I I   X Q   Q E B
_ BALL AT THE

M X I X Z B   T B X O
PALACY! WEAR

V L R O   C X S L R O F Q B
YOUR _ _ _ _ _ _ _ _ _ _

M X O Q V   A O B P P
_ _ _ _ _   _ _ _ _ _ !

87

Roxie's Cookie Wands

Roxie's fairy kitchen is a wonderful place to be. There really is nothing better than the warm smell of biscuits baking in the oven! These scrumptious cookie wands are made out of shortbread and lolly sticks.

You will need:

- 200g butter
- 300g plain flour
- 1 tsp vanilla extract
- 100g caster sugar
- 2 eggs
- 4 lolly sticks, soaked in water
- A star-shaped cookie cutter
- 125g granulated sugar
- Food colouring

1
Cut the butter into chunks. Add the flour, vanilla extract and caster sugar. Mix the ingredients together until they bind into a sweet dough.

2
Sprinkle flour on the worktop, then roll out the dough until it is as thick as your finger. Use the cookie cutter to press out star shapes.

3

Push a lolly stick firmly into each star. Place the shapes on a baking tray, then pop them in the fridge for 15 minutes to chill.

4

Put the wands into the oven for about 10-12 minutes, until they turn golden brown. Then leave them to cool completely.

5

Ask a grown-up to help you separate the eggs into yolks and whites. You won't need the yolks, so set them aside in a different bowl.

6

Add a few drops of your favourite food colouring to the granulated sugar. Stir it all together until the colour is even throughout.

7

Use a pastry brush to paint every cookie star with egg white. Sprinkle on the coloured sugar. Once dry, your wands are ready to enjoy!

Magical Masks

At your next birthday party, why not ask your guests to create and wear their own magical masks?

You will need:
- White card
- Pencil
- Felt-tip pens
- Sequins
- Scissors
- PVA glue
- Curling ribbon

1
On a piece of card, draw a face outline that is slightly bigger than your own. Cut the shape out and hold it up to your face, then mark where the eyes should go. Carefully snip out some peep holes.

2
Hold the mask back up to your face, then sketch where the nose sits. Now carefully cut off the bottom half of the mask so that your mouth becomes visible.

3
Use your brightest felt-tip pens and sparkly sequins to decorate the mask with hearts, butterflies and stars.

4
Now make a small hole on either side of the fairy mask.

5
Thread a long piece of curling ribbon through one of the holes and tie it in a knot at the back of the mask. Repeat on the other side, then tie the ends together behind your head.

6
Take the mask off, then ask a grown-up to curl the ribbon ends with the scissors.

91

Fashion Disaster!

The Fashion Fairies have mislaid their magical items!
Can you help to find them? Draw lines to match the
fairies to their objects.

Hairbrush

Necklace

Lola the
Fashion Show
Fairy

Claudia the
Accessories
Fairy

Matilda the
Hair Stylist
Fairy

Backstage
Pass

PASS

Pen

Brooke the Photographer Fairy

Lipstick

Tyra the Dress Designer Fairy

Tape Measure

Alexa the Fashion Reporter Fairy

Camera

Miranda the Beauty Fairy

Find out if you're right on Page 205

93

Pretty Pirouetting Tutu

Do you love to point your toes and dance? If you do, then this twinkly pink tutu could be just the thing to wear for your next performance. When you pop on the graceful net skirt you'll feel like the most beautiful ballerina in the world!

You will need:
- 1 metre of net fabric
- Hole punch
- 1 metre of thin ribbon
- Jewels and sequins (optional)
- PVA glue

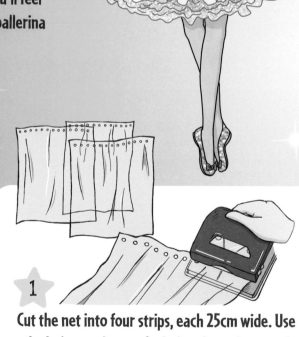

1

Cut the net into four strips, each 25cm wide. Use the hole punch to make holes along the top of each strip. The holes should be about 2cm apart.

Thread the ribbon in and out of the holes. This will be the waistband of your tutu.

3

Join the strips of net by overlapping the last five holes of one strip with the first five holes of the next, and thread the ribbon through both strips.

4

When you've threaded the ribbon through all the holes, gently pull on both ends to gather the net until it fits round your waist. Leave an equal amount of ribbon at each end for a bow.

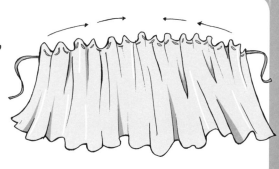

5

Decorate your tutu by using a dab of PVA glue to stick jewels and sequins onto the net. (Make sure your decorations are not too heavy!) Leave to dry.

6

Tie the ribbons into a pretty bow round your waist. Then leap and twirl, just like a prima ballerina!

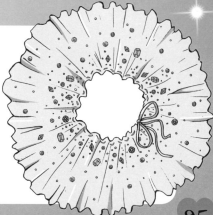

95

What Kind of Fairy Friend Are You?

We all need friends – they make every day sparkle! Bubbly, shy or happy-go-lucky – what sort of friend are you? Take this special quiz and find out!

At school, your favourite subject is...
- ☐ A. Science
- ☐ B. English
- ☐ C. PE
- ☑ D. Art

1

Your dream birthday gift would be...
- ☐ A. A digital camera
- ☐ B. A chapter book
- ☐ C. A box of magic tricks
- ☑ D. A cuddly teddy

4

At the weekends, you like to...
- ☐ A. Travel somewhere new
- ☐ B. Watch a movie
- ☐ C. Go to a party
- ☑ D. Visit the petting zoo

2

Your favourite colour is...
- ☐ A. Purple
- ☐ B. Lilac
- ☐ C. Orange
- ☑ D. Yellow

5

You'd describe your fashion as...
- ☐ A. Practical and bright
- ☐ B. Soft and pretty
- ☐ C. Fun and quirky
- ☑ D. Cute and comfy

3

You and your friends love...
- ☐ A. Discos
- ☐ B. Meals out
- ☐ C. Skating in the park
- ☑ D. Sleepovers

6

Mostly As
YOU'RE A LOVABLE LEADER
You're just like Izzy the Indigo Fairy! Your friends turn to you for advice – an important friend indeed.

Mostly Bs
YOU'RE AN EAGER EAR
You and Angelica the Angel Fairy are very special. You're the best listeners around!

Mostly Cs
YOU'RE A FUN-TIME FRIEND
You and Una the Concert Fairy are very similar – you both know just how to set the party mood!

Mostly Ds
YOU'RE A HAPPY HUGGER
Everyone likes a hug! You and kindly Anya the Cuddly Creatures Fairy are truly to be treasured.

Fairy Ludo

How to play:

• Photocopy the counters on the right and cut them out.

• Take turns throwing the die. Each counter needs a six before it can leave its corner.

• If you land on someone's counter, they have to go back to their corner. They have to throw another six before they can come out again.

• The winning fairy is the first player to get all of their counters through the square in the middle and safely off to Fairyland!

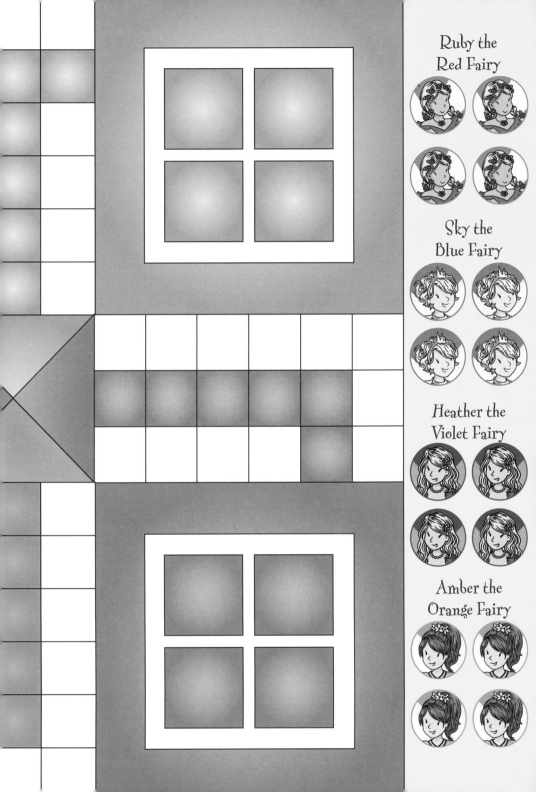

Ruby the
Red Fairy

Sky the
Blue Fairy

Heather the
Violet Fairy

Amber the
Orange Fairy

Fun at the Festival

Three cheers for Daisy the Festival Fairy! Every summer she patrols fields, parks and farms, making sure that festivals are fun places to be. Kirsty and Rachel have taken a snap of the fairy to stick in their secret memory books. One picture is perfect, but something's not quite right with the other one – six things have changed. Has Jack Frost been meddling again? Stop the Ice Lord's mischief by drawing a circle around each of the magical mistakes. Can you find them all?

Find out if you're right on Page 205

Spells and Goblins

How to play

♥ Choose a counter each, then throw the die. The person with the highest score gets to start first.

♥ Take turns to work your way up the board. If you land at the bottom of a trail of fairy stars, swoosh your counter all the way up to the top. If you land at the top of a grouchy goblin, you'll have to move all the way down to his toes.

♥ Good luck! The winner is the person who gets their counter to the home square first.

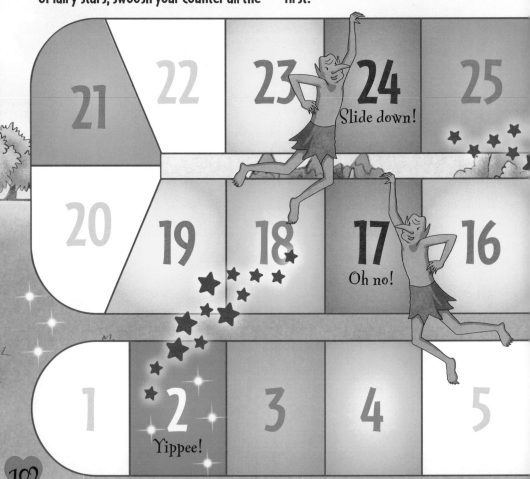

21 22 23 24 Slide down! 25

20 19 18 17 Oh no! 16

1 2 Yippee! 3 4 5

Have you ever played Spells and Goblins? It's the Rainbow Fairies' favourite game! All you need are some counters, a die and someone to play with. Who can get to the top of the board first?

HOME!

34

33

32
Unlucky!

31

26

27
Yippee!

28
Bad luck!

29

30

15
Wooo!

14

13

12

11
Follow the stars!

6
Yeahhhh!

7

8
Lucky you!

9

10

Eye Spy

Feast your eyes on this wonderful scene of the Fairyland Palace Gardens.
Everyone is having a fantastic time tending the gardens and enjoying
the sunshine. Look at the picture carefully and tick the boxes when
you have found everything listed.

Can you spot:

- ☑ **One mole**
- ☑ **Three butterflies**
- ☑ **Seven magic wands**
- ☑ **Two birds**
- ☑ **Eight carrots**
- ☑ **One dolphin**
- ☑ **Five bumblebees**
- ☐ **Two goblins**

Dance Delights

Jade the Disco Fairy uses her enchanted Dance Ribbon to make sure that everyone can enjoy fun times on the dance floor! Find a friend and have a go at learning this latest routine. Jade's good friend Ruby the Red Fairy shows you how it's done!

1
Take one step forward, then one step back, with your arms outstretched. Repeat this four times, moving in time with the beat.

2
Do a twirl to the right, taking care to finish as neatly as possible.

3
Cross your feet over, whilst wiggling your shoulders to the music.

4
Uncross your feet again, then raise your arms up, shimmying your fingers all the way.

5

Clasp your hands over your chest and then move them in and out to the beat four times.

6

Take one step forward, then one step back with your arms outstretched. Repeat this four times.

7

Hold both arms out to your left, then swing them across your body to the right, twinkling your fingers.

8

Raise both hands above your head, then roll them down to the floor whilst wiggling your body to the beat!

9

Do a twirl to the left, waving your arms up and down like a butterfly.

10

Take eight steps to the left, clicking your fingers in time.

11

Take eight steps back to the right, clicking your fingers again and smiling to the tune.

12

Finish with your head down and arms outstretched, then wait for the applause!

Goblin Tangle

Jack Frost is not happy. His silly goblins have managed to get themselves into a terrible tangle! Can you count how many goblins there are?

Find out if you're right on Page 206

109

Lacey's Little Mermaid Make-It

Lacey is a very thoughtful fairy. Whenever one of her friends has a birthday coming up, she makes them a little homemade gift. The fairies love her mermaid peg dolls – they're irresistible! Have a go at making a Lacey dolly. She'll look gorgeous on your bookcase or bedroom shelf!

You will need:
- A wooden clothes peg
- Poster paint
- Paintbrush
- Fine-tipped pens
- Pencil
- Purple craft foam
- Scissors
- Strong glue
- Tracing paper
- Brown embroidery thread
- PVA glue
- Silver glitter

1

Hold the top of the peg between your finger and thumb and paint on the front of Lacey's purple tail. Rest it on the newspaper to dry.

2

Paint in the fairy's crop top above the tail. Now turn the peg over and paint the other side to match.

3

Take a fine pen and carefully draw a little face onto the peg.

110

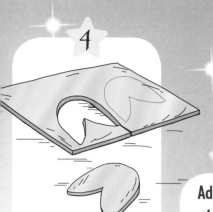

4

Cut out a tail shape from a piece of craft foam. Cut a second tail out to match. Stick the shapes together to make them extra thick.

5

Add glue to the top of the tail and slot into the base of the clothes peg. Hold it there until the glue dries.

6

Draw a pair of wings onto a sheet of tracing paper. Cut the wings out, then stick them onto Lacey's back.

7

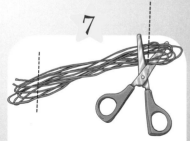

Cut a bunch of embroidery threads about 10cm long. Fold the bunch in half, then glue the folded bit to the top of Lacey's head.

8

Cover Lacey's tail with glue and sprinkle it with glitter. Shake the excess off and say hello to your lovely Lacey dolly!

Toadstool Gift Box

Most fairies live in tiny toadstools, with cheery red-spotted roofs. This lovely toadstool gift box will make the perfect home for your treasures or jewellery. You could pop it beside your bed and imagine that your favourite fairy is sleeping in a house next to you!

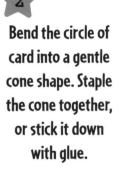

You will need:
- Saucer
- Pencil
- Cardboard
- Scissors
- Stapler
- PVA glue
- Crepe paper
- White paper
- Kitchen roll tube
- Felt-tip pens

1

Place the saucer on a sheet of cardboard and draw around it with a pencil. Cut a slit from the outside edge into the centre.

2

Bend the circle of card into a gentle cone shape. Staple the cone together, or stick it down with glue.

3

Put the saucer on red crepe paper and draw a slightly larger circle. Cut out and stick on the cardboard cone. Fold the paper underneath and glue it in place.

4

Draw some small spot-shaped circles on to white copy paper. Cut these out and stick them onto the red cone roof.

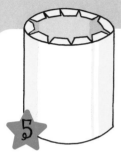

6

Place the saucer on another piece of card and draw round it again. This time, cut the circle out and cover it with green crepe paper.

5

Cut the kitchen roll tube in half. Glue white paper all over it. Cut 1cm slits around one end of the roll and bend those tabs into the centre.

7

Take the roll and sit it tab-side down on the green circle. Dot glue on the folded tabs and stick it onto the grassy base with the tabs in the centre.

8

With a bright felt-tip pen, draw some pretty fairy flowers growing up the toadstool, plus a little door and some windows.

9

Put the red roof in place and your gift box is ready! Use it to store tiny objects, like rings, hair clips and secret spells.

113

I Spy Fairies!

It's a busy day in the Palace kitchens – it's Queen Titania's birthday! There are going to be parties all over Fairyland. Peep at the happy scene, then answer each of the quiz questions.

1. What colour is Melodie's apron?
PINK

2. What type of fairy are Ruby and Sky?
Rainbow Fairies

114

3. Who is doing the dishes?
2 birds

4. How many helper bees can you find?
5

5. How many layers of cake are there?
4

6. What's inside the starry gift box?
4 teddy

7. Who is peeping through the window?
A. goblin

115

Spot the Fairies!

The fabulous fairies at the top of the page appear in exactly the same order on only one of the below rows. Can you find them and circle them?

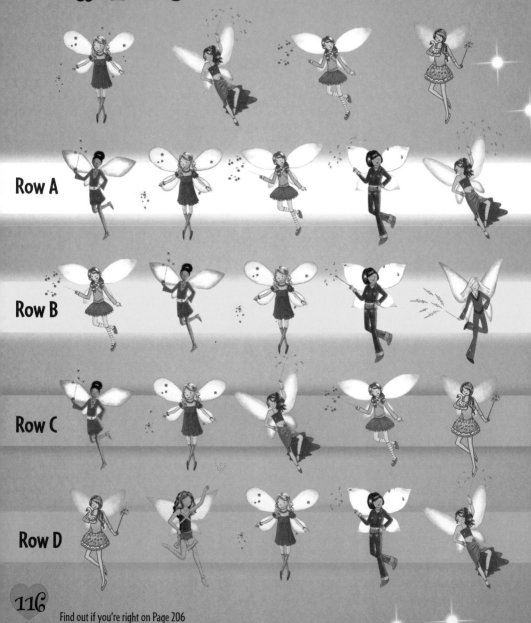

Row A

Row B

Row C

Row D

Find out if you're right on Page 206

Dive In!

Samantha the Swimming Fairy's heart is all a-flutter! Can she swim her way to the end of the maze? Find a pen or pencil, then draw a line to show Samantha the quickest way through the water.

START!

Lovely Bug Canapés

Fairies love to nibble on tiny treats that they can pick up
and eat on the go! Here is one of Elisa the Adventure Fairy's
favourite canapé recipes. They're perfect for sharing with
your friends at street parties and festivals.

You will need:
- Cheese spread
- Salted crackers
- Carrot sticks
- Pretzels

Kitchen Careful
Always ask a grown-up helper to help with cutting and using the hob – that way no one can hurt themselves.

1

Squeeze some cheese spread onto the top of a salted cracker.

2

Gently push two pretzels into the cheese spread. Set them at an angle so they form a pair of insect wings.

3

Carefully stick two tiny carrot sticks into the cheese in front of the wings. These are your bug's antennae!

Which Fairy Are You?

Tick your favourite fairy from each row on the opposite page. You can then work out what sort of fairy you are using the decoder below.

If you ticked mostly...

Blue Shapes

You are a quieter fairy. You like fun and games, but enjoy chilling out too.

Red Shapes

You are a fun-loving fairy through and through. You love parties and dancing!

Yellow Shapes

You love bright colours, giggling and spending time with your friends.

Purple Shapes

You love to make up great games and stories to share with your friends.

Earn Your Fairy Wings

You're a true friend of Fairyland, so you should have your very own fairy wings! Follow these steps to magic up your own beautiful wings. But remember, you will need the help of a grown-up for the cutting and sewing!

You will need:

- Baking sheet
- 1.5 metres craft wire
- Strong sticky tape
- The legs from an old pair of tights
- A piece of soft, pretty fabric
- Acrylic paints
- Ribbon, needle and thread
- Glue, sequins and glitter
- Elastic

1

Shape the craft wire into a circle and fasten the ends together with tape.

2

Twist the wire circle in the middle so that it looks like a number 8. Use some more tape to hold it in this position.

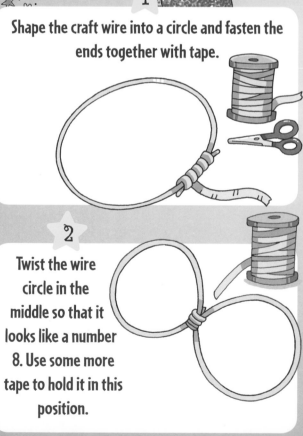

3

Now you can create your very own wing shapes! Bend each side of the 8 to make your perfect wings.

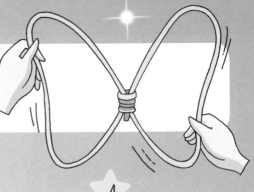

4

Then take one leg from the tights and stretch it over the first wing. Tie the open end of the leg at the place where the two wings meet. Repeat for the second wing.

5

Tie a piece of fabric around the centre of the wings to hide the tape and knots.

6

Now you can decorate your fairy wings! Use the paints, ribbons, sequins and glitter to make pretty patterns. Leave the wings to dry.

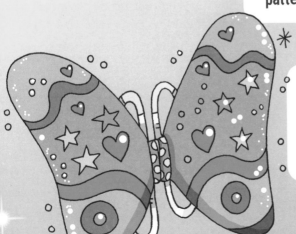

7

Cut two lengths of elastic for armholes. When the wings are dry, sew the elastic onto the back.

C is for Crossword

Fluttery butterflies! This page is full of fairies with one thing in common. Can you guess what it is? Look at the pictures and read the clues. Now use a pen to complete the crossword. Chloe the Topaz Fairy has sprinkled a few letters onto the grid to get you started.

Across

1._____
the Snow
Fairy

2._____
the Reef
Fairy

3._____
the Christmas
Tree Fairy

4._____
the Cupcake
Fairy

7._____
the Sunflower
Fairy

Down

1._____
the Snow Cap
Fairy

2._____
the Accessories
Fairy

3._____
the Clownfish
Fairy

5._____
the Ice
Bear Fairy

6._____
the Chocolate
Fairy

124

Why not create your own crosswords for you and your friends to complete?

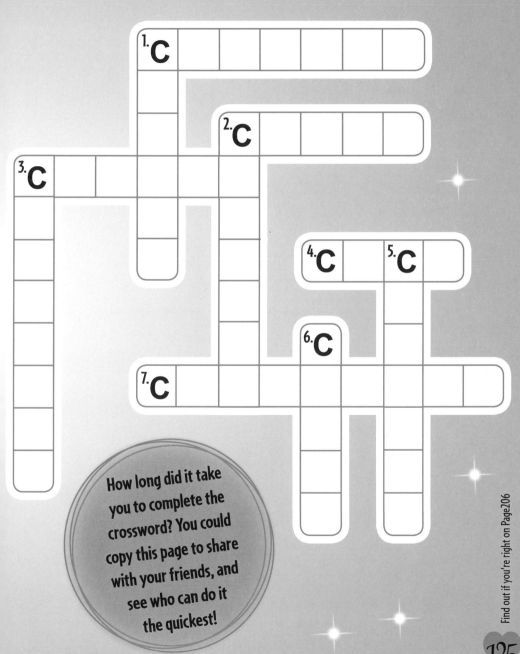

How long did it take you to complete the crossword? You could copy this page to share with your friends, and see who can do it the quickest!

Find out if you're right on Page 206

Memory Magic

Look at this picture of Fairyland for one minute and try to remember what you see. Then answer the questions on the next page.

1. Who is standing beside King Oberon?
2. How many goblins are in the picture?
3. Who is Rebecca the Rock 'n' Roll Fairy dancing with?
4. How many toadstool houses are there?
5. Who is standing next to Kirsty?

127

Zadie's Pretty Pincushion

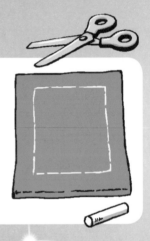

Zadie's fairy pincushion is ever so handy – it slips on her wrist so she never loses her needles and pins. Would you like to make one, too? Choose your favourite fairy colours, then get stitching!

You will need:
- Chalk
- Ruler
- Felt in 2 colours
- Scissors
- Cereal packet
- Pencil
- Embroidery yarn
- Needle
- Fabric stuffing
- Elastic
- Cotton

1

With your chalk and ruler, measure out an 8cm x 6cm rectangle on one of the felt pieces. Ask a grown-up to help you cut it out.

2

Take the second piece of felt and measure out a 7cm x 5cm rectangle. Draw a 6cm x 4cm rectangle on the cereal packet. Ask a grown-up to help you cut these out, too.

3

Lay the bigger piece of felt on a clean table, then place the second piece on top so that it sits neatly in the centre.

4

Thread a needle with the yarn. Carefully sew up three sides of the small piece of felt so that it sits on the big piece like a pocket.

5

Slot the card into the pocket to rest against the bigger piece of fabric. Pop some stuffing inside. Sew the pincushion shut.

6

Wrap a piece of elastic around your wrist. When you have a length that fits, carefully cut it to size.

7

Stitch both ends of the elastic to the back of the felt. Your fairy pincushion is ready to wear!

129

Swirly Dance Ribbons

This ribbon wand makes Jessica the Jazz Fairy want to dance, dance, dance! It is perfect for a special performance, but just as much fun to play with in your bedroom. Try making patterns in the air and then surround yourself in swirls – it's irresistible!

You will need:
- 2 or 3 narrow ribbons (1 metre long)
- Piece of tissue paper (30cm square)
- Sticky tape
- 1 straw
- PVA glue
- Glitter to decorate (optional)

1

Squeeze a pea-sized blob of glue on one corner of the tissue paper and lay a straw just below it. Wrap one layer of tissue paper tightly round the straw.

2

Paint a strip of glue alongside the straw and wrap the tissue paper round again. Repeat so there are three layers of tissue paper. Cut off the extra paper.

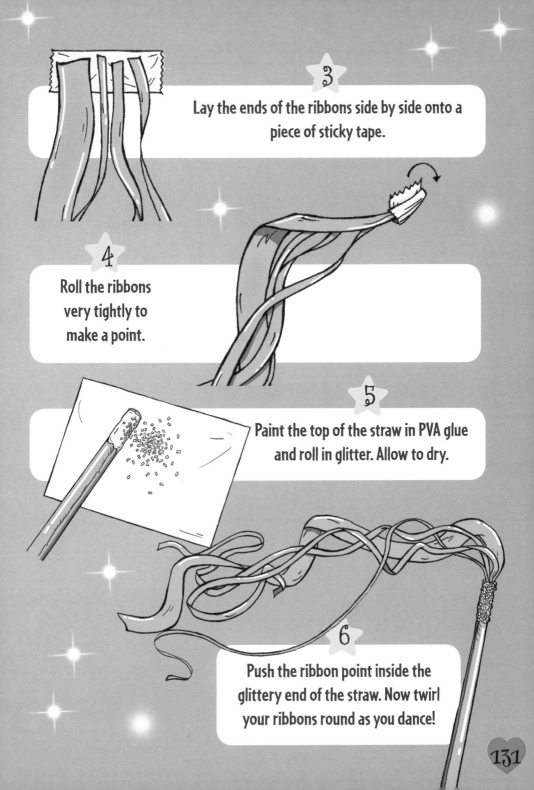

3

Lay the ends of the ribbons side by side onto a piece of sticky tape.

4

Roll the ribbons very tightly to make a point.

5

Paint the top of the straw in PVA glue and roll in glitter. Allow to dry.

6

Push the ribbon point inside the glittery end of the straw. Now twirl your ribbons round as you dance!

131

Marissa's Fizzing Fountain

Last New Year's Eve on the stroke of midnight, Marissa had a surprise for her Fairyland friends. She lit up the evening air with an amazing golden fountain! Would you like to magic one up? It really is enchanting!

SSH!
FAIRY SECRET
In her science lessons, Marissa teaches fairies how this magic really works. The fountain happens when the baking soda and vinegar react together inside the glass vase!

You will need:
- Small glass vase with a thin neck
- Baking soda
- Yellow food colouring
- Gold glitter
- A deep baking tray
- 125ml vinegar

132

Make sure you leave lots of space around your fountain, so it doesn't make a mess!

1
Measure out three tablespoons of baking soda, then tip it into the vase.

2
Next add a few drops of yellow food colouring and two teaspoons of glitter.

3
Take your vase and baking tray outside. Put the baking tray down on the ground and carefully stand the vase up in the middle of it.

4
Pour out the vinegar into a measuring jug.

5
When you're ready for the sparkles to be-gin, quickly pour the vinegar into the vase. Stand a few steps back and wait for the fountain to fizz!

133

Garden Fun

Charlotte the Sunflower Fairy would like to show you how to have lots of fun with flowers and plants. Here's how to grow your own sunflowers! Plant seeds in little pots on your windowsill, then give them to your friends!

Don't forget to tell your friends to look after their seedlings! When the plants reach 10cm tall they can be planted.

You will need:
- Empty yoghurt pots
- Poster paint
- Paintbrush
- Stickers or ribbon
- Compost
- Sunflower seeds
- Plastic food bags
- Lolly sticks
- Felt-tip pens

1

Cover the yoghurt pots with brightly coloured poster paint. Stand the pots upside down to dry.

2

Decorate the pots with cute stickers, or tie a ribbon round them in a bow.

3

Fill each pot with compost and make a hole about 2cm deep. Pop one seed into the hole and cover it with compost. Sprinkle a little water on the top.

4

Carefully put the pots into clear plastic food bags and seal them up. This will help the seeds stay warm. Store your pots in a dry, dark place.

5

When the first leaves begin to bud, remove the bags and put the pots on a sunny windowsill. Give them a little water every day.

6

Write each of your friends' names on a wooden lolly stick and push them into the pots. Your gifts are ready to be handed out!

Musical Wordsearch

GUITAR

VIOLIN

HARP

FLUTE

DRUM

Victoria the Violin Fairy would love to play you some beautiful music while you try to find all the musical words in the jumble of letters below. They could run up, down, across, backwards or even diagonally!

PIANO

G	U	I	T	A	R	H	P	V	A	N
A	E	H	Q	K	T	F	I	B	I	T
M	C	L	A	M	E	J	L	L	Z	J
H	N	F	T	P	N	O	O	U	H	L
A	V	E	N	I	R	I	Q	I	T	U
R	S	T	O	A	V	Z	N	L	E	E
P	M	F	H	N	G	L	X	Y	I	Y
S	C	E	N	O	H	P	O	X	A	S
T	W	L	N	D	I	A	U	C	P	I
G	P	M	U	R	D	L	D	Y	O	A
U	D	D	N	E	M	T	I	C	S	G

Find out if you're right on Page 206

SAXOPHONE

Dreamcatcher

Sabrina the Sweet Dreams Fairy looks after a special bag of dream dust that makes sure fairies and humans have only happy dreams. Help her make a dreamcatcher to keep away nightmares!

You will need:
- A paper plate
- Scissors
- Hole punch
- Ruler
- Felt-tip pens
- 2.5m wool or thin ribbon
- Beads & buttons
- Three craft feathers
- Silver glitter
- Glue

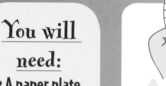

1

Cut the inner circle out of the paper plate, leaving the rim. Try not to snip through the edge!

2

Use your hole punch to make single holes all around the rim of the paper plate about 2cm apart.

3

Choose your favourite pens and cover the plate in bright, happy colours. You could draw stripes or little moons or stars!

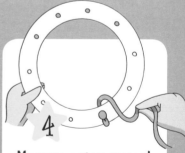

4

Measure out your wool or thin ribbon and thread one end through one of the holes on the plate.

5

Weave the wool or ribbon in and out of the holes in any direction you like. You can also thread in pretty beads and buttons!

6

When you reach the end of the wool or ribbon, tie it securely at the back of the plate.

7

Hold your dreamcatcher upright and punch three holes along the bottom of the plate.

8

Tie three more pieces of ribbon to the holes at the bottom and thread some beads onto each. Then knot a coloured feather at the end.

9

Dot glue around the bottom of the dreamcatcher and sprinkle silver glitter all over the glue. Then shake the excess glitter off.

10

Make two holes at the top and thread a loop of wool or ribbon through to make a hook.

139

Fairy Charm Rings

It's so hard to find jewellery to fit fairy fingers! These little rings are so easy to make, and they can be threaded with all sorts of beads and buttons. When Scarlett the Garnet Fairy puts her rose-coloured one on, her dress and shoes look extra special!

You will need:

• A roll of thin elastic cord (either rainbow-coloured or sparkly is pretty!)
• Selection of beads and buttons
• Scissors

1

Tie a knot in a piece of the elastic. Thread a small bead or button onto the elastic. Make sure the knot is big enough so the bead or button doesn't slip off.

2

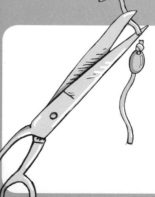

Trim off the elastic above the knot. Repeat four or five times, using different coloured elastic and different beads or buttons.

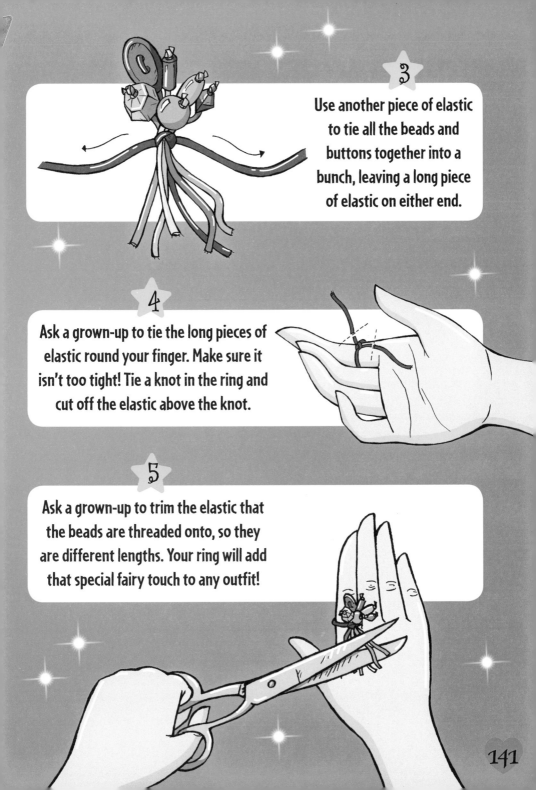

3

Use another piece of elastic to tie all the beads and buttons together into a bunch, leaving a long piece of elastic on either end.

4

Ask a grown-up to tie the long pieces of elastic round your finger. Make sure it isn't too tight! Tie a knot in the ring and cut off the elastic above the knot.

5

Ask a grown-up to trim the elastic that the beads are threaded onto, so they are different lengths. Your ring will add that special fairy touch to any outfit!

Hidden Gems Wordsearch

Jack Frost has stolen the jewels from Queen Titania's crown! Can you find the seven Jewel Fairies and their jewels in this wordsearch?

```
F  L  C  E  R  I  H  P  P  A  S
A  E  H  Q  K  T  B  I  B  P  T
M  C  L  A  M  E  J  Y  E  Z  J
E  N  O  T  S  N  O  O  M  H  L
T  V  E  N  D  R  E  Q  I  A  U
H  S  T  O  P  A  Z  N  L  E  C
Y  M  F  H  K  G  L  X  Y  I  Y
S  C  A  R  L  E  T  T  U  H  O
T  W  I  N  D  I  A  R  C  P  I
G  E  M  E  R  A  L  D  Y  O  A
U  D  D  N  O  M  A  I  D  S  G
```

Find out if you're right on Page 206

| INDIA, MOONSTONE | SOPHIE, SAPPHIRE | EMILY, EMERALD |

| AMY, AMETHYST | CHLOE, TOPAZ | LUCY, DIAMOND | SCARLETT, GARNET |

Dancing Dilemma Crossword

Tasha the Tap Dance Fairy has waved her magic wand and created a crossword about her friends! See if you can answer the questions and fill in the spaces.

Find out if you're right on Page207

Across

1. Rachel's surname!
2. The name of the village where Kirsty lives
3. The name of the Ice Dance Fairy
4. Finish the name of this fairy: Jade the _ _ _ _ _ Fairy

Down

1. How many Dance Fairies are there?
2. Kirsty's best friend
3. Name the Rock 'n' Roll Fairy
4. What have the goblins stolen from the Dance Fairies?

143

Fairyland Tiara

Queen Titania loves wearing the Fairyland crown jewels, and her tiara is her favourite of them all! Why not make a silvery one just like it, and decorate it with twinkly gems? It will be truly unique and fit for a fairy queen!

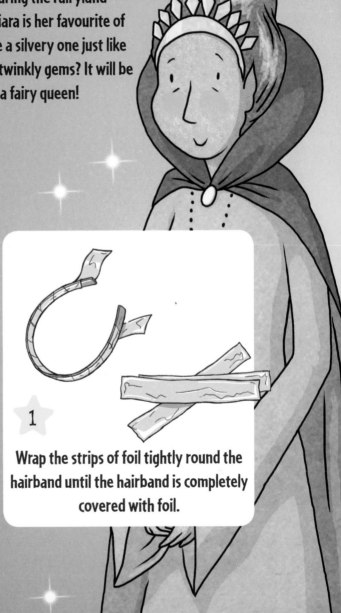

You will need:
- Strips of aluminium foil approx 2cm wide
- A thin plastic hairband
- Sticky tape
- Jewels or sequins to decorate your tiara (optional)
- PVA glue (optional)

1

Wrap the strips of foil tightly round the hairband until the hairband is completely covered with foil.

2

Squeeze the ends of the foil together and tuck them under the hairband. Cut off any excess foil to make it neat and tidy.

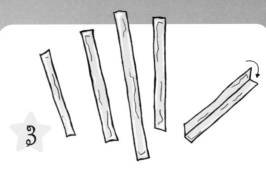

3

Cut five strips of foil: two strips 10cm long; two strips 8cm long; one strip 12cm long. Fold them in half lengthwise with the shiny side out, and then in half again.

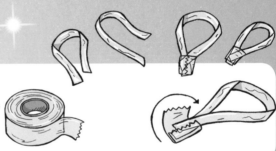

4

Bend each foil strip into a loop. Stick the ends together with clear sticky tape.

5

Fix the loops to the back of your tiara with sticky tape. Put the biggest loop in the middle, the medium-size loops on either side, and the smallest ones at each end.

6

Stick on jewels and sequins with PVA glue to make an extra-special tiara twinkling with fairy magic.

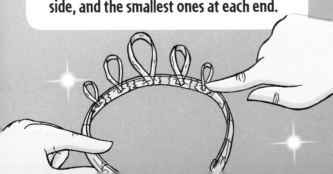

Fairy Cakes

This is Coco the Cupcake Fairy's favourite cupcake recipe, straight from her Fairyland kitchen! These fairy cakes look lovely when they are piled into a multi-coloured stack and then dotted with candles.

You will need:

- 125g margarine
- 125g caster sugar
- 1 tsp vanilla extract
- 2 large eggs
- 125g self-raising flour
- 12 cake cases
- 100g icing sugar
- Food colouring
- Cake decorations
- A mixing bowl

1
Ask a grown-up to heat the oven to 180°C, Gas Mark 4 or 360°F. Set 12 cake cases out on a baking tray.

2
Put the margarine and sugar in a mixing bowl and cream together with a fork.

Your birthday is the one day of the year when every human is given a secret helping of Rainbow Magic. Don't forget to make a wish!

3
When the mixture is smooth and a pale yellow colour, add the vanilla extract. Now beat in the eggs and add the flour a little at a time.

4

Gently spoon some cake mix into each of the cases and bake them for 20 minutes until they are golden brown.

5

When your birthday cupcakes are cool, mix 100g of icing sugar with a little water and add a drop of colouring. Spread some icing over each cake and then decorate.

Race to Fairyland

You can play this game with one or two fairy friends. You need four coins or buttons each, and a die. Decide which of these three fairies you want to be and place all your counters on her picture. Whichever player has a birthday next begins. Throw the die in turn and move clockwise around the board, starting on the coloured shape close to your fairy. You can start with a new counter at any time. The aim of the game is to fly all your counters to the Fairyland Palace before anyone else! They must all be there to win.

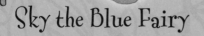

Sky the Blue Fairy

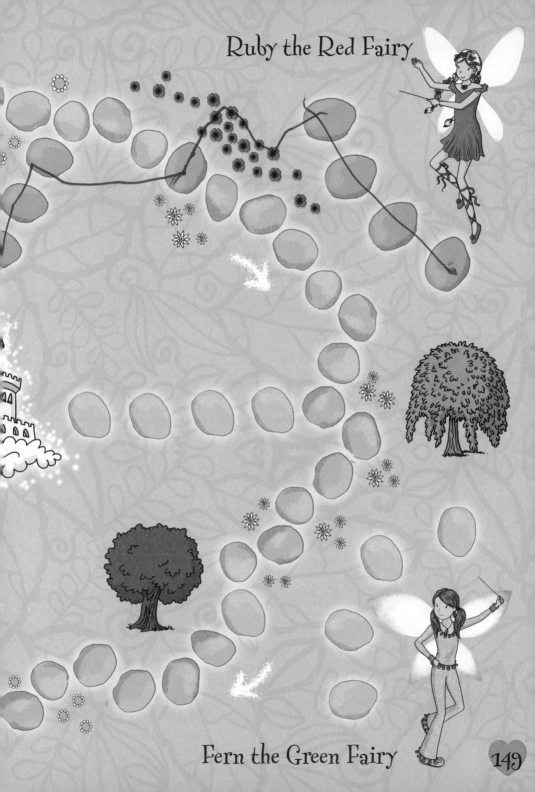

Ruby the Red Fairy

Fern the Green Fairy

149

Perfect Pizza

Roxie the Baking Fairy loves making these delicious fairy-sized pizzas – they are the perfect snack for a party!

See how many delicious toppings you can pile onto each one!

You will need:

- 1 muffin
- 2 tbsp tomato-based pasta sauce
- 2 tbsp Cheddar cheese
- Toppings of your choice, for example: sliced peppers, olives, fresh tomatoes or cooked sausage

1

Ask a grown-up to help you slice the muffin in half. This will give you two round pizza bases.

Don't forget to use ingredients that are lots of different colours, to make your pizza look truly splendid!

2

Cover each base with tomato pasta sauce. Add toppings, such as peppers, olives, fresh tomatoes or cooked sausage.

3

Sprinkle on the cheese. Ask a grown-up to help you cook your pizzas under a medium grill for approximately five minutes until the cheese is melted and bubbling. Yummy!

Memories to Treasure

Pippa the Poppy Fairy has come up with a great way of saving your most precious memories. She's made a time capsule! Why not make one of your own? Imagine what fun it will be to open in ten years' time!

You will need:

- A family-size biscuit tin
- Scourer
- A tea towel
- Old newspapers
- Brightly-coloured spray paint
- Permanent marker pens
- Stick-on gems,
- Sticky tape
- Scissors

1
If the tin has stickers on it, soak in warm soapy water before scrubbing with a sponge scourer.

2

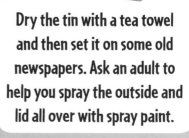

Dry the tin with a tea towel and then set it on some old newspapers. Ask an adult to help you spray the outside and lid all over with spray paint.

Why not ask your friends and family to write something to put in the time capsule?

3
Write your name on the lid with a permanent marker pen.

4

If you'd like to, decorate the tin with stick-on gems, or draw some Rainbow Magic fairies and glue them round the sides. The tin is going to hold some of your most precious memories, so it needs to look really special.

5

When your tin is ready, it's time to fill it up. Only you can decide what to put inside! Try to imagine what you would be interested to discover in ten years' time.

6

When you've packed up your tin, fit the lid back on top. Fix a layer of tape all around the rim to make a seal.

7

Put it somewhere you'll be able to find again in 10 years. You could bury it in a flowerbed, or in the loft.

Olympia's
Spot the Difference

Olympia the Games Fairy loves posing for pictures! She has printed two photos of herself, but five things are different in the right-hand picture. Can you spot them all?

True or False?

Have a good look at this happy fairy scene and decide whether the statements below are true or false.

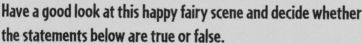

1. Ruby the Red Fairy and Olivia the Orchid Fairy are having tea inside the old black pot.

2. Izzy the Indigo Fairy is sitting inside the log.

3 There are fourteen fairies in this scene.

4 The bees are playing with Danielle the Daisy Fairy.

5 The ladybird has a pink tummy.

6 Jack Frost is spying on the fairies from the pond.

Fairy Marshmallow Cake

Sienna the Saturday Fairy's favourite afternoons are spent nibbling treats and sharing secrets with her best friends. When she invites fairies over, they always ask her to make this special marshmallow cheesecake – it's lighter than air and deliciously sweet! This scrumptious recipe is just the thing to serve after a plate of fairy sandwiches and a glass of juice.

You will need:

- 125g digestive biscuits
- 75g soft butter
- 350g marshmallows
- 175ml full fat milk
- Plastic food bag
- Cake tin
- Rolling pin
- Bowl
- Saucepan
- Wooden spoon
- 225g full fat soft cheese
- 450ml whipping cream
- Crumbly chocolate bars to sprinkle on top

1
Snap the digestive biscuits in half, then pop them into a plastic food bag.

2
Tie a knot at the top of the bag and tap it with a rolling pin until the biscuits are all evenly crushed.

158

3

Pour the biscuits into a bowl and mix in the soft butter.

4

Scoop the biscuity mixture into a cake tin with a removable base. Now use the back of a spoon to flatten the mixture so that the base is evenly covered. Pop the tin into the fridge.

5

Put the marshmallows and milk into a non-stick saucepan, then ask an adult to help you gently heat it until the marshmallows have melted.

6

Take the warm marshmallow mixture and pour it into a glass bowl.

7

Add the soft cheese to the bowl and stir it with a wooden spoon.

8

While this mixture is cooling, pour the whipping cream into a separate bowl and beat it with a fork or electric whisk, until it forms fluffy peaks. Gently fold the cream into the marshmallow sauce.

9

Pour the mixture onto the biscuit base in the tin and put it into the fridge again. Let it cool for at least three hours.

10

Take the cheesecake out of the fridge and sprinkle chocolate on it. Take out of the tin and onto a pretty serving plate!

A Shivery Scene

This is a picture of Jack Frost's Ice Castle. Brave fairies sometimes venture up the icy path to invite Jack Frost to parties, but they don't stay long as it's so cold. Brrr! Have a good look at this chilly scene, then turn over the page and answer as many of the questions as you can without peeping!

160

How much do you remember?

1. How many geese did you count?

2. What is the goblin doing?

3. What colour is the goblin's hat?

4. How many brave fairies are in the picture?

5. What is the goblin sitting on?

6. How many windows did you count in the Ice Castle?

Frosty Figure

Oh dear! Jack Frost thinks he is a great artist, but he is terrible. He's trying to draw a picture of himself, but it keeps coming out wrong! Annabelle the Drawing Fairy has decided to help him out. Using a pencil, carefully copy each square in the grid on the left into the matching blank panel on the right.

Florence's Friendship Bracelet

Florence the Friendship Fairy urgently needs your help! Jack Frost has stolen the magical bracelet that she uses to look after friendships. Can you make her another one?

You will need:
- Embroidery thread in four pretty colours
- Ruler or tape measure
- Scissors
- A4 clipboard

1

Unravel a length of thread in each of the four colours, cutting it off at around 60cm.

2

Hold the four threads together and tie a knot about 3cm from the top.

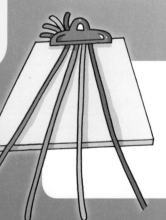

3

Lay the clipboard on the table in front of you and clip the knot in place at the top. Fan the four threads out in front of you.

4

Take the far left thread and loop it over and then under the thread next to it. Hold the second string straight, then pull the first string tight to form a knot.

5

Repeat step 4 again so that you make a double knot in your bracelet.

6

Using the same first thread, work your way along making double knots in each of the colours. By the time you have finished, the thread will have moved across to the far right on the clipboard.

7

Now take the new far left thread and do the same thing again, tying double knots all the way across the colours.

8

Keep on knotting until the bracelet is long enough to go round your wrist. Gather the strings together, then tie the ends in a tight knot.

Fairy Favourites

What's the best thing about being a fairy? Is it casting spells and wishes, attending Fairyland banquets, or fluttering through clouds and sliding down rainbows? Use this quiz to discover what you'd like best if you could be a Rainbow Magic fairy for a day.

1. You've just arrived at a birthday party! Do you...
A. Make a beeline for your best friend?
B. Start the dancing off by twirling across the room?
C. Find a mirror to check your party dress looks just right?
D. Put your hand up straightaway to lead the first game?

2. Pick your favourite school subject from the list below.
A. Creative writing.
B. Drama.
C. Art.
D. PE.

3. Where would you rather go on holiday?
A. A quiet cottage in Cornwall.
B. A big group holiday somewhere hot.
C. A Paris city break.
D. The theme parks of Florida.

4. Which of these things would you be most likely to do?

A. Enter a poetry competition.
B. Organise a surprise party.
C. Put together a fancy-dress outfit.
D. Take trampolining lessons.

5. Which of these possessions is the most precious to you?

A. Your latest book.
B. Your photo album.
C. Your sparkly hair bands.
D. Your bike.

Mostly As
WHISPERS OF MAGICAL THINGS!
You're shy on the outside, but inside your wonderful imagination is sparkling with fairy spells and wishes.

Mostly Bs
A FAIRY FOR SPECIAL OCCASIONS!
Top of everyone's invitation list, you adore the thought of and attending the Fairyland Midsummer Ball!

Mostly Cs
TINY TOES AND FAIRY FROCKS!
You're a fairy fashionista - your notebooks are full of scribbles of shimmery dresses, silk slippers and sparkly tiaras.

Mostly Ds
THERE SHE FLUTTERS!
Kirsty and Rachel have such adventures flying around with the Rainbow Magic fairies – you'd love to try it too!

167

Funky Headband

Did you know that you can wear this headband two ways? The fabric side looks really funky, but when Ashley the Dragon Fairy fancies adding a bit more colour to her outfit, she turns the band over to show the seven colours of the rainbow!

You will need:

- A piece of fabric (6cm wide)
- Narrow rainbow ribbons (1 metre long)
- Fabric glue

1

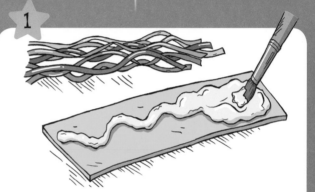

Cut the length of fabric to fit over your head from ear to ear. Spread some glue onto the back of the fabric with a brush.

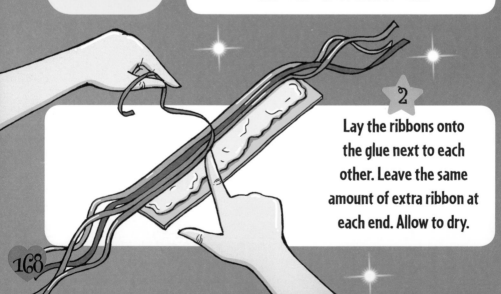

2

Lay the ribbons onto the glue next to each other. Leave the same amount of extra ribbon at each end. Allow to dry.

Wear as a headband, tying the ribbons under your hair at the back. You can wear it showing the rainbow ribbon side or turn it over to show off the funky fabric.

Why not make lots of different headbands for your family and friends to wear?

169

Saffron's Suncatcher

Saffron the Yellow Fairy loves the sunshine, and always hangs a suncatcher in her window. Follow these instructions to make a magical suncatcher for your bedroom window.

You will need:

- 2 small sheets of black card
- Red, blue, yellow and green cellophane
- Scissors
- Glue
- Pencil
- Hole punch
- Ribbon

1

Draw four different shapes onto one sheet of black card. Ask an adult to put the two sheets of card together and cut out the shapes.

2

Choose pieces of cellophane that are a little bit bigger than the shapes in the card. Glue the cellophane over the shapes in the first sheet of card. Choose a different colour for each shape.

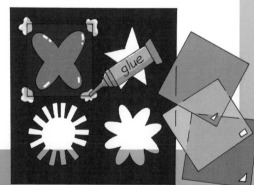

3

Put a line of glue around the edge of the first sheet of card. Stick the second sheet of card over it.

glue

4

Use the hole punch to make four holes along the top of the suncatcher.

5

Loop the ribbon through the holes and ask a grown-up to tie it to the middle of your curtain rail.

171

Green Goblin Cheesecake

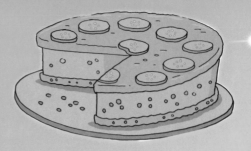

Cherry the Cake Fairy invented a delicious new recipe especially for Jack Frost's green meanies. The creamy cheesecake needs chilling instead of baking, so it's just the thing to whip up in Jack Frost's Ice Castle. Give this recipe a whirl – it's so simple even a silly goblin could make it!

You will need:
- 180g plain digestive biscuits, broken into crumbs
- 1 tablespoon demerara sugar
- 100g soft butter
- 250g full fat soft cheese
- 50g icing sugar
- 1 teaspoon vanilla extract
- A few drops of lime juice
- Green food colouring
- 2 fresh kiwi fruit

1

Ask a grown-up to find a medium-sized springform baking tin. This is a round tin with a clip that allows it to open up when the cheesecake is ready to serve.

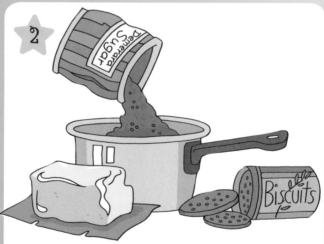

2

Place the biscuits, demerara sugar and butter into a non-stick saucepan. Take turns with your helper to gently stir the ingredients until the butter has melted.

3

Carefully tip the buttery biscuit crumbs into the baking tin. Use the back of a wooden spoon to press the mixture evenly all around the base. Pop the tin into the fridge to keep cool.

4

Find a large mixing bowl, then measure out the soft cheese, icing sugar and vanilla extract. Mix everything together until it is smooth and creamy. At first the cream cheese might seem a bit stiff, but it will soon loosen up.

5

Ask your grown-up helper to cut a fresh lime in half, then squeeze a good few drops into your cheesecake topping. Mix everything together once again, then try a tiny mouthful. The mixture should taste sweet with a slight citrussy tang.

6

Now carefully stir in just one or two drops of green food colouring. If the colour is still pale when you have finished, slowly add a drop at a time until you get the right shade of goblin green!

7

Take the baking tin out of the fridge and spoon the green mixture over the base. Smooth the topping out, then put it back in the fridge to chill. Goblin chefs need to be patient – the cheesecake will take at least a few hours to set. When you have taken it out, peel and slice the kiwi fruit. Arrange the slices on the top of the cheesecake and Cherry's mouth-watering creation is ready to serve!

Beautiful Bridesmaid

Doesn't Mia the Bridesmaid Fairy look pretty? If you study these five pictures very carefully you'll see that one of them is slightly different from the others. Can you work out which is the odd one out?

A.

B.

C.

D.

E.

DID YOU KNOW?
Mia and Kate the Royal Wedding Fairy are the best of friends!

Find out if you're right on Page 206

175

Josie's Jangly Bangles

Josie can often be spied fluttering around Fairyland, delivering her handmade trinkets. These colourful bangles make such a thoughtful gift.

You will need:

- Lolly or wooden craft sticks
- Drinking glass
- Emery board
- Old newspapers
- Poster paint
- Paintbrush
- PVA glue
- Glitter
- Clear varnish
- Sequins, gems or glitter

1
Ask a grown-up to boil a kettle, then lay your lolly sticks down in a heatproof dish.

2
When the kettle is ready, ask your helper to pour hot water over the lolly sticks. Leave the sticks to soak for 45 minutes.

3

Carefully pick the lolly sticks out of the water and bend with your fingers. If they don't curve easily in your hand, put the sticks back in the dish and do steps 1 and 2 again.

Gently bend each stick into a curve. Then slide each into a thin glass so that it holds its shape. Leave the glass on the windowsill or beside a radiator to dry out overnight.

When the curved sticks are dry, slip them out of the glass. If there are any rough edges, sand the sticks with an old emery board.

Spread out some newspaper and then paint the bangles in pretty colours.

When the bangles are dry, it's time to work your fairy magic! Stick on some sparkly gem shapes, sequins and glitter.

177

Fairies in Danger

Six Rainbow Magic fairies are stuck in Jack Frost's Ice Castle! Can you unscramble their names so that Queen Titania can magic them back to the Fairyland Palace?

ARFOL THE
NACYF SREDS FAIRY

— — — — — the

— — — — —

— — — — — Fairy

LITEJU THE
NIVLATEEN FAIRY

— — — — — — the

— — — — — — — — —

Fairy

SICHIERS THE
SHWI FAIRY

_ _ _ _ _ _ _ _ _ _

the _ _ _ _ Fairy

GPEAI THE
EMMINOTAP FAIRY

_ _ _ _ _ _ the

_ _ _ _ _ _ _ _ _

Fairy

ALETSL THE
RAST FAIRY

_ _ _ _ _ _ _

the _ _ _ _ Fairy

ELITANA THE
SMACTIRSH
GOKSTING
FAIRY

_ _ _ _ _ _ _

the

_ _ _ _ _ _ _ _ _ _

_ _ _ _ _ _ _ _

Fairy

Find out if you're right on Page 207

179

Wonderful Windmills

Olivia the Orchid Fairy loves making these flowery windmills! They're great for a blustery day. The bright, spinning colours always cheer her up as they remind her of times spent playing in the sun with her Petal Fairy friends!

You will need:

- Piece of card 15cm square
- Piece of paper 10cm square
- Plates, jars or egg cup to help draw perfect circles (optional)
- Pin
- Bead
- Pencil
- Scissors

1

On the piece of card, draw a circle 15cm across. Draw a smaller circle inside the first one 11cm across. Cut out the larger circle.

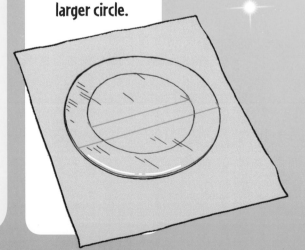

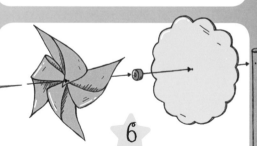

Draw small circles around the edge and cut around the outsides to make a flower.

Fold your paper in half to make a triangle. Then fold in half again, making another triangle.

Open the paper and mark a pencil dot on each of the folds 15mm from the centre. Cut along the folds up to the dots.

Curl the right-hand corners of each triangle into the middle and ask a grown-up to secure all the corners with a pin through the middle of the paper.

Now push the pin through the bead, then through the centre of your flower shape, and finally, 1cm from the top of a pencil. Blow your windmill and watch it spin!

Fairy Tresses

Whenever Imogen the Ice Dance Fairy wants to dress up her hair, she slides in this rainbow hair decoration! Don't worry if you've got short hair, the flowing ribbons set off any style. The clips are wonderful for when Imogen is performing – she loves the way they flutter as she glides round the ice rink!

You will need:
- Selection of rainbow-coloured ribbons, wool and lace
- Small elastic band
- Hairclip

1

Cut a selection of rainbow-coloured ribbons, wool and lace to about 5cm longer than your hair.

Bunch them together and secure with a small elastic band about 5cm below the top.

3

Cut a piece of ribbon about 30cm long and clip it inside your hairclip.

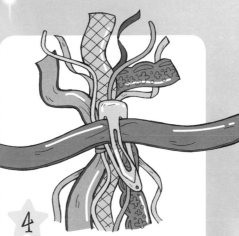

4

Slide the back of the hairclip through the elastic band.

5

Tie the long ribbon around the decoration and make a pretty bow at the front. Clip the fairy tresses into your hair or onto a ponytail.

More Fairy Magic!

Fiona the Flute Fairy has made a special wish, and is flying to deliver it to Chrissie the Wish Fairy. She has written it in special fairy code, because there are goblins about and she wants her wish to be secret! Can you read her wish by using the special code below?

Fiona's Wish

— — — — — —

— — — — — —

— — — — — —

— — — — — —

Find out if you're right on Page 207

Petal Personality

The Petal Fairies are always busy keeping their blooms beautiful! Answer the questions in this flowchart to find out which flowery fairy you're most like.

Alone

Are you happiest alone or in a crowd?

Crowd

Do-er

Are you a do-er or a dreamer?

Dreamer

Fashion

Do you prefer fun fashion or old favourites?

Faves

186

Do you prefer to be a trendsetter or everyone's friend?

Trendsetter → Hot-house flower

Friend → Big-hearted bloom

Are you happiest centre-stage or behind the scenes?

Stage → Rare beauty

Behind → Queen of the garden

Is your style classic or funky?

Classic → Ray of sunshine

Funky → Super in scarlet

Do you like garden games or country walks?

Games → Flowery friend

Walks → Blushing bud

Olivia the Orchid Fairy
An eye-catching beauty who always attracts a crowd!

Pippa the Poppy Fairy
A kind and caring team player. Stunning both inside and out.

Ella the Rose Fairy
Sometimes shy, but blessed with natural grace and a sweet manner.

Danielle the Daisy Fairy
The good-hearted girl-next-door whom everybody loves to love!

187

Fairy Friendship Necklace

Phoebe the Fashion Fairy has designed this stunning pendant make-it for you to share with your best friend. Follow the easy steps to create two original handmade necklaces!

You will need:

- Baking sheet
- Silver foil
- Non-toxic modelling clay
- Cocktail sticks
- Rolling pin
- Small heart-shaped cookie cutter
- Old newspapers
- Acrylic paints
- Paintbrushes
- Large blunt needle
- Thin ribbon
- Scissors

1
Ask a grown-up to pre-heat the oven to 130°C/250°F/Gas Mark 1. Line a baking sheet with silver foil and put it to one side.

2
Pull off a small lump of clay and knead it gently with your fingers to soften it up.

3
When the clay becomes easy to shape, roll out 12 marble-sized balls.

4
Carefully push a cocktail stick through each bead for the ribbon to go through later. Place your beads on the baking sheet.

5

Roll out a piece of clay approx 2cm thick then gently push a small heart-shaped cookie cutter into it twice to make two pendants.

6

Push the cocktail stick through each heart to make a good-sized ribbon-hole. Keep the hole near the top.

7

Add the hearts to the foil-lined tray and ask an adult to pop this in the oven for 25 minutes.

9

Thread the needle with a length of coloured ribbon, then thread 3 beads through in alternate colours. Now add one of the heart pendants and 3 more beads.

8

When the baked clay pieces have cooled completely, paint them in a variety of pretty colours. Leave everything to dry overnight. The next morning, paint your name on one heart and the name of your best friend on the other heart, using a thin paintbrush.

10

Take the other piece of ribbon and make up the second heart necklace in the same way.

11

Give your best friend the necklace with your name on it. Now you wear the one with her name on it, so everyone knows you are friends forever!

189

Show What You Know!

The Weather Fairies have devised this quiz to work out how well you know your best friend! Sit on your own and try to answer as many questions as you can. When you've finished, ask your best friend to mark your answers and total up your scores. You score one point for each correct answer.

What does she like for breakfast?

What colour are your friend's eyes?

Which clubs does she belong to?

What outfit is she most likely to wear?

What's her favourite pop group?

What's her best subject at school?

Where did she last go on holiday?

What is her favourite colour?

What colour is her bedroom?

What's the name of her oldest cuddly toy?

What is her favourite food?

What's on her pencil case?

Describe her funkiest party outfit!

Which TV show does she like best?

What is her greatest talent?

Name the most surprising thing about her.

Write down her silliest nickname.

Name her favourite hobby.

Where was her last birthday party?

What sort of books does she read?

Scores 0-6

It's a promising start, but there's more to discover about your best friend! It's time to do lots more listening to find out all the things that make her tick.

Scores 7-14

Your friend still holds a few secrets, but maybe you're still getting to know each other? Keep chatting and sharing and you'll have full points in no time!

Scores 15-20

Well done, you really do know your friend inside out! You're the very best of friends and clearly share everything together.

191

Sun and Snow Spellcaster

Sun or snow – which would you prefer? Each night, turn this decoration to show the fairy forecast you'd like for the next day, then hang it on your bedroom door. If you're lucky, your weather wish might just come true!

You will need:

- 2 rectangular pieces of card approximately 25 cm x 10 cm (ideally pale blue and dark blue)
- PVA glue
- Scissors
- Small bowl and egg cup
- Paint, coloured paper, cotton wool and sequins to decorate

1

Paint the card. One piece should be pale blue and the other dark blue. Stick the two pieces of card together. Allow these to dry.

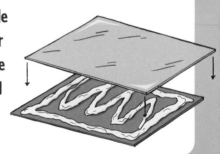

2

Using the small bowl as a guide, draw an arc at the top of your card. Cut around the arc so the end of the card is rounded.

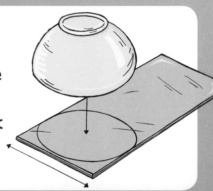

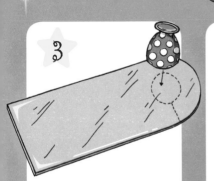

3

Use an egg cup to draw a small circle near the rounded end of the card. Cut a line from the edge of the card to the small circle and cut out the small circle.

4

On the pale blue side, paint a rainbow at the rounded end. Make fluffy clouds using cotton wool or white paper. Paint or glue on a sun and sunbeams.

5

On the dark blue side, stick sequins and cotton wool to make snowflakes and cloudy skies. Hang the spellcaster on your doorknob and see if you can predict the weather. Will it be sunny or snowy?

193

Shannon's Ocean Jellies

Shannon the Ocean Fairy is in charge of Fairyland's three enchanted pearls – without them, daytime and nighttime get completely mixed up! She is friends with all sorts of wonderful water creatures, from tiny seahorses to dancing dolphins.

You will need:

- 135g lime flavoured jelly
- Blue food colouring
- 4 clear glass tumblers
- Penny sweets, such as jelly sharks, fish and fruit shoelaces
- Squirty dairy cream

1

Break the lime jelly into chunks, then place into a bowl. Ask a grown-up to help you make up the jelly according to the packet instructions.

2

While the jelly mixture is still hot, gently trickle in a drop or two of blue food colouring. Mix everything together with a spoon until it turns a bluish green – the colour of the ocean.

After around an hour, the jellies should still be soft. Take the glasses out and quickly push some penny sweets into each of them. You could use jelly fish shapes plus fruity shoelaces to form seaweed.

4

Put the glasses back into the fridge until the jelly is completely set.

5

Before you serve your ocean jellies, spray each one with a swirl of dairy cream. This wave tops off your underwater desserts!

Florence's BFF Quiz!

All of the Rainbow Magic fairies are super friendly, but who would be your best fairy friend (BFF) in the Rainbow Magic world? Take the quiz below to find out.

Which of these flowers do you like the best?

A. Poppy
B. Rose
C. Iris
D. Sunflower

What is your favourite animal?

A. Dog
B. Cat
C. Pony
D. Rabbit

How would you describe your personality?

A. Confident
B. Friendly but shy
C. Funny. You love to make people laugh!
D. Relaxed and easy-going

What do you like to do the most on a Saturday night?

A. Make up dance routines and listen to music
B. Chill out with your friends in your bedroom
C. Write jokes and stories
D. Read your favourite fairy book

What is your favourite colour?

A. Red
B. Pink
C. Purple
D. Yellow

Mostly As – Your BFF is Una the Concert Fairy
You're happy and have lots of energy, just like Una! You're also very loyal and always stand by your friends.

Mostly Bs – Your BFF is Mia the Bridesmaid Fairy
You're very friendly with a gorgeous smile, just like Mia! You look after your friends and would never give away a secret.

Mostly Cs - Your BFF is Leah the Theatre Fairy
You and Leah both have a brilliant sense of humour. You're confident but also like time to chill out on your own.

Mostly Ds – Your BFF is Hannah the Happy Ever After Fairy
You have a wonderful imagination. You and Hannah would make great writing partners! Your pals always love to spend time with you.

197

Make Your Own Tiara Topper

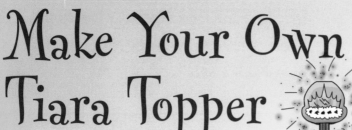

Whenever they sign royal decrees, King Oberon and Queen Titania always use jewel-topped pens and pencils! They have given special permission for you to have one, too. Follow these instructions to make a twinkly royal tiara to sit at the top of your favourite pencil.

You will need:

- Tracing paper
- White card
- Scissors
- Felt-tipped pens or coloured pencils
- Glitter pen and stick-on gems
- Strong glue or sticky tape

1

Lay a sheet of tracing paper over the King and Queen's tiara template, then trace round the shape as neatly as you can.

2

Put the tracing paper over a sheet of white card and draw over the markings. Carefully cut the template out of the card.

3

Use your pens and pencils to decorate both of the tiaras. Add extra gemstones, pearls and patterns.

4

When you've finished drawing, use a glitter pen and stick-on gems to give your topper even more sparkle!

5

Carefully fold the topper along the dotted line in the middle. Ask a grown-up to help you stick or tape the topper onto the end of your pencil. Your twinkly tiara is ready to use!

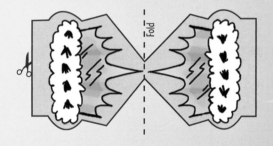

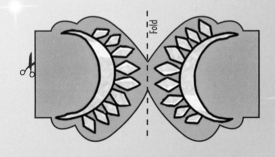

Jewelled Hairband

The feathers in this ponytail band turn everyday hair into something fantastic! Amy the Amethyst Fairy uses one to tie up her blonde curls – she loves the way the beads match her necklace. Try making this band to go with your favourite party outfit!

You will need:

- Thin elastic cord (preferably in a pretty colour)
- A ponytail band
- Thin ribbon
- Beads and feathers (either rainbow colours or match the colours of your favourite Rainbow Magic fairy!)

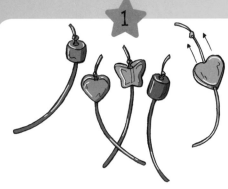

1

Cut a 6cm length of elastic for each bead. Tie a knot in each end. Thread on the bead and cut off the elastic above the knot.

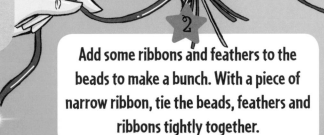

2

Add some ribbons and feathers to the beads to make a bunch. With a piece of narrow ribbon, tie the beads, feathers and ribbons tightly together.

DID YOU KNOW?
Amy loves hanging out with her friends the Fashion Fairies!

3

Using the same ribbon, tie the bunch of beads, feathers and ribbons onto the ponytail band and knot to secure. Trim the ribbon to the same length as the elastic cords.

DID YOU KNOW?
Amy's friend Matilda the Hair Stylist Fairy helped her design this hairband.

201

Heidi's Hide-and-Seek

Heidi the Vet Fairy never has a moment to spare! Every morning she puts on her blue vet's coat and flutters out to look after the animals in Fairyland. Ten things from Heidi's vet surgery are hiding somewhere in this grid. Can you help Madeleine the Cookie Fairy find them all?

THERMOMETER

COLLAR

BLANKET

CHART

MEDICINE

TABLE

BASKET

STETHOSCOPE

SCALES

BANDAGE

S	N	M	E	D	I	C	I	N	E	K	D
G	T	R	U	E	G	A	D	N	A	B	K
B	H	E	S	E	T	I	C	S	Q	U	F
J	P	S	T	Z	E	Y	T	E	R	A	J
E	A	W	J	H	T	A	B	L	E	Z	I
K	X	M	U	R	O	H	T	A	V	Y	B
T	N	T	A	V	Q	S	V	C	W	M	L
E	X	H	S	K	C	D	C	S	B	D	A
K	C	O	I	X	J	Z	P	O	L	H	N
S	L	C	O	L	L	A	R	Q	P	R	K
A	F	T	V	U	M	T	G	D	N	E	E
B	R	E	T	E	M	O	M	R	E	H	T

Find out if you're right on Page 207

Answers

JUMPING JACK FROST

Jack loves:
SNOW
GOBLINS
COLD
HAIL
BLUE

Jack hates:
SUNSHINE
FAIRIES
LAUGHTER

P18

POP STAR PUZZLE
P24

Image D

ALMOST BEDTIME!
P28

SILLY SPEAK

Florence the Friendship Fairy - C
Honor the Happy Days Fairy - B
Juliet the Valentine Fairy - E
Tamara the Tooth Fairy - F
Trixie the Halloween Fairy - D
Shannon the Ocean Fairy - A

P40

PERFECT PAIRS

P54

A MAGICAL MYSTERY!
P48

Kate the Royal Wedding Fairy

A ROYAL MESSAGE
P86

Please come to a ball at the palace!
Wear your favourite party dress.

204

P62

WAND WORDSEARCH

E	A	S	T	E	R	E	G	G	N	N
D	G	N	I	N	T	H	G	I	L	
R	I	B	F	T	C	W	G	U	K	
Y	P	A	X	S	H	E	L	L	C	
I	E	D	M	N	M	K	D	E	I	
L	N	H	V	O	L	D	C	P	T	
R	O	X	A	Z	N	B	L	T	S	
H	E	A	R	T	L	D	O	V	P	
J	Z	K	W	Q	S	G	C	F	I	
S	N	O	W	F	L	A	K	E	L	

ANIMAL MATCH-UPS

P76

Katie has a Kitten called Shimmer
Bella has a Bunny called Misty
Georgia has a Guinea Pig called Sparky
Lauren has a Puppy called Sunny
Harriet has a Hamster called Twinkle
Molly has a Goldfish called Flash
Penny has a Pony called Glitter

P80

SPOT THE DIFFERENCE

FASHION DISASTER

P92

Fashion Disaster!

P104

EYE SPY

Eye Spy

P100

FUN AT THE FESTIVAL

Answers Part 2

GOBLIN TANGLE

P108
15 Goblins

SPOT THE FAIRIES
P116
The four fairies appear in Row C

C IS FOR CROSSWORD
P124

I SPY FAIRIES!
P114
1. Pink
2. Rainbow Fairies
3. Two birds
4. Five
5. Four layers of cake
6. A teddy bear
7. A goblin

DIVE IN!
P117

BEAUTIFUL BRIDESMAID
P174
Image C is the odd one out

MUSICAL WORDSEARCH
P136

HIDDEN GEMS WORDSEARCH
P142

206